Inventions
from the Shed
Shed

Inventions from the Shed

TEXT BY
JIM HOPKINS

PHOTOGRAPHY BY
JULIE RILEY

HarperCollins*Publishers New Zealand Limited*

To 'The Puffin'

Anyone wishing to contact the inventors
featured in this book can do so by writing to:

'Inventions from the Shed'
c/- HarperCollins Publishers
PO Box 1
Auckland

Mark the envelope with the name of the intended recipient.

First published 1999
HarperCollins*Publishers (New Zealand) Limited*
P.O. Box 1, Auckland

Text copyright © Jim Hopkins, 1999
Photographs copyright © Julie Riley, 1999,
except where indicated

Jim Hopkins and Julie Riley assert the moral right
to be identified as the authors of this work.

ISBN 1 86950 323 6

Designed by Jan Harris
Typeset by Pauline Whimp
Printed by Australian Print Group

Acknowledgements

Looking for inventions is a bit like trying to find needles in a haystack when you're wearing a blindfold and boxing gloves. Without some very good guides and some very good leads we would have had no choice but to give up, admit defeat and donate our organs to a charitable trust of the publishers' choice in a final act of abject penance. So, on behalf of our livers and kidneys, we'd like to sincerely acknowledge and gratefully thank the individuals and groups listed below.

First and foremost, all the inventors who let us into their sheds and shared their secrets. Your generosity equals your ingenuity and we hope this book does justice to both. Thanks also to those other inventors who would've liked to have been involved but had to keep things under wraps.

Tom Barter from The Inventors Trust, who gave us copious helpings of advice, contacts and patient good humour. The Trust can be contacted at Private Bag MBE #248, Auckland.

The following thorough and helpful patent attorneys who put us in touch with inventors or inventors in touch with us.

Elspeth Buchanan from P.L. Berry & Associates
Don Hopkins from Don Hopkins Patent Attorneys
Bill Howie and Corinne Blumsky from A.J. Park & Son
Kate Wilson from James & Wells

Simon Angelo, organiser of the first New Ideas Expo in 1988 and another who helped us find the good inventions. Simon plans a second Expo, to run from the 29-31 of October 1999 at the Greenlane Exhibition Centre in Auckland. Unless a crazed gunman turns up, or there's a big demo, it probably won't attract much media attention, but if you're interested in what the sentient minority are up to, try to get there.

Ian Watt and Sue Page from HarperCollins. The literary equivalents of Captain Kirk and Lieutenant Uhura, they've kept this Enterprise boldly going where it hadn't thought it would, even when it seemed certain to disappear down a black hole or up its own Warped Factor. And it was all done through the power of their own forceful field. Not even the accountants could disturb their equilibrium or imperil their sangfroid.

Tess and Tom, who tolerated all the trips away and even managed to endure the crazy times at home. Ken, who adapted so well to frequent absences.

All the other friends and family members who the shared the trials or lent a hand along the way.

PS Thanks to the compassionate couple from Kaitangata who drove us back to the gas station in Herbert when we ran out of gas just south of Oamaru.

Jim Hopkins and Julie Riley

Introduction

You need to know that this is going to be an interactive introduction. In a moment, you'll be asked to close your eyes. Not yet, you understand, not yet. Quite apart from the fact that you may be at the helm of a supertanker, if you did it now you wouldn't know why you were. You wouldn't have seen the words that explain the purpose of this small but essential exercise. And it's pretty straightforward – the purpose I mean. Well, so is the exercise. All we need is a little imagination. And all we seek is a little understanding.

So, here's what I'd like you to do. At the end of this sentence, just relax, close your eyes and try to imagine the person you would call a 'typical inventor'.

Then open your eyes again. Sorry, I should've mentioned that before we faded to black. However, let's assume you're with us and that the image of your 'typical inventor' is still fresh in your mind. Chances are, you've come up with a character, a bloke, who could be described as a cross between Albert Einstein, Dr Who and the Nutty Professor. Someone with electric hair and eccentric temperament, prone to wild-eyed expostulations and the quoting of abstruse formulae. If you got as far as visualising the setting your inventor was in, then he was probably surrounded by steaming retorts and blinking dials and busily tinkering with a device combining the best features of a Victorian steam laundry and a UFO.

Now, if I've got that wrong, if I've misrepresented your imagining, then I apologise. But inventors say the stereotype in the last paragraph is the sort of thing they have to live with. And they don't like it. That became very obvious very quickly in the course of researching this book. Making contact with inventors, their suspicion was tangible. We'd endeavour to explain the aim of the exercise and there'd be a pause, a guarded silence. Then the oft-repeated question, 'This isn't going to be a send-up, is it?' Because that's what so many have come to expect. Reports that present them as looneys or crooks, part of some dotty sideshow way out on the fringe. They say it's virtually impossible to get any serious coverage of what they do.

That's a view shared by those who work with inventors, advising them on copyrights and patents and licensing and all the other essential elements of the activity. One patent attorney put it as succinctly as anyone. What was actually extraordinary about inventors, she said, was that they weren't extraordinary at all. By and large, they were quiet and unassuming citizens, realistic, conscious of their responsibilities to family and community and trying, in their own way, to improve their own situation and add something to other people's. A bit like a doctor at a party, they didn't advertise their preoccupation. Indeed, said the attorney, the neighbours of her clients would probably be astonished to discover they had an inventor living next door. They might've heard the odd bang, clatter and thud coming from the shed but, like as not, assumed it was routine lawn mower maintenance and not the exertions of an aspiring innovator. As a general rule, they're not making time machines or death rays or matter transporters. Chances are, they're trying to build a better lawn mower. Because that happens to be what they like doing, or are driven to do. It's a noble, but sometimes frustrating obsession. The thing is, inventors have got the 'Bloke Bug' – even if they're not all blokes. They're gripped by that compulsive curiosity, that urge to tinker and meddle and dismantle and reassemble that is bedded somewhere in our genes. While for others the passion may be golf or bird watching or collecting

Gordon's self-tilting trailer

thimbles, for inventors, it happens to be the challenge of creating new things that just might make a difference.

And they do. Inventions do have the capacity to transform. Forget the biggies for a moment, don't think about the bomb or electricity, or genetic engineering or even Gutenberg's modest contribution, the printing press. Just imagine what your world would be like without Band Aids, or Velcro, or staples, or Aspirin, or pens with their own ink, or EFTPOS, VCR's, CD ROMs, ABS, GST, smoke alarms, insurance, microwave meals, electric irons, seat belts, the stuff that keeps stains out of carpets, disposable nappies, cordless phones, acrylic paints, Teflon, fibreglass Batts, chip boards, skateboards, Leggo, Lotto, Ludo, Play Doh or any of the other things that you regard as more important than those included in this grossly incomplete list.

Whatever the examples, the point is plain. We live in an invented world. And we should be taking our own inventors more seriously. Because they're good. And they're clever. And their inventions are things that can enhance and improve and just occasionally transform the way we live. The proof's in the pages beyond this. I defy anyone to look through this book and not find at least ten things that make them say, 'Gee, I want one of those.'

Unfortunately, as any inventor will tell you, that doesn't guarantee much. Assuming the prototype became a product, you might still want it. You might even buy it, if the price is right, if the packaging catches your eye and if the ads catch your attention. Which points to what many inventors see as their biggest challenge. Inventing's easy, they say. It's getting an idea out of the shed and into the shops that's the big job. Especially when the inventor tries to do it alone. The wise ones know when to let go, when to bring in outside expertise. But that can be hard. And so can a clear-headed assessment of an idea's true commercial potential. 'Inventors have huge blind spots,' says someone closely involved with an internationally successful invention. 'They've given birth to their baby and that's it. They can't see it objectively. I've never met a mother yet who said, "This baby's ugly." But sometimes you have to. The fact is, only one invention in ten or even one in twenty is going to make money.'

Of course, making money means spending it as well. Which isn't easy to do when you haven't got a lot. And when you can't find too many people, if any, who are willing to help. 'The job of inventing is an extremely uphill one in New Zealand,' says one who's persisting anyway. 'There are virtually no incentives from the government or the corporate sector.' Some say that absence of incentives is actually a disincentive. They believe tax changes or more government funding is necessary. Others are not so sure. They're not convinced bureaucrats would pick good inventions any better than they might select winning Lotto numbers. They say what's really needed is smarter bank managers. Now that, on the face of it, may seem to be an oxymoron, but hope springs eternal. Although no one wants the wait to be that long. Nor do they wish to wait indefinitely for an end to what they see as a persistent inertia in business, a blindness to the possibility that something could actually be done here if it's not being done overseas. Those who lead the mighty corporations now happily enmeshed in the global economy are, they say, ignoring an asset that's here, right under their noses. And that they should be forging partnerships so that that asset and its benefits can be developed and shared.

It might be tempting to dismiss all of this as special pleading. Except for the fact that there is a track record here, there is strong evidence that we do come up with worthwhile ideas and inventions. Sure, we may get carried away with our ability to fashion world peace and a winning World Cup combination out of a bit of 4 x 2 and some No. 8 fencing wire. But that's understandable. It's the kind of defensive reaction you'd expect from a country still growing up, still somewhat dependent on the good opinions of others. Like any adolescent, we still need a bit of approval and, when we don't get it, we resort to a bit of bluster.

And yet we really don't need to. Any objective assessment of the last hundred years throws up an impressive list of ground-breakers and mind-movers. Most New Zealanders would have, or should have, at least a sketchy knowledge of our inventive trinity, Ernest Rutherford, Richard Pearce and Bill Hamilton. We know the atomic age was born in a tin shed at Canterbury University where Rutherford began the work that ended in the bomb bay of the Enola Gay. We know that Richard Pearce, working alone, under-rated, underfunded and still not fully appreciated, achieved something quite awesome, whenever his plane got into the air. And we know the unique propulsion system of the Hamilton jet boat has made waves right around the world.

But how many of us know much of William Pickering, apart from the fact he spent a lot of years at NASA, or indeed anything of Francis Tripp, the DNA pioneer? Does the name Bertram Ogilvie ring a bell? It should do. The next time you fly, take a look at those bits at the back of the wing that go up and down, the 'flaps' or ailerons. Bertram Ogilvie invented them, and he was the

Chris's Hyperion aircraft

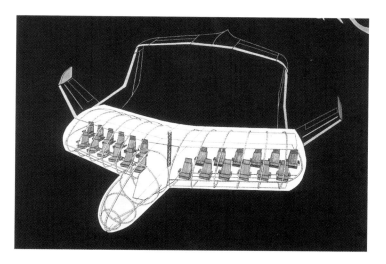

first person in the world to fly a plane that used them. That was in Napier, where he tested and improved his idea in the years between 1907 and 1910. A chance encounter with Lord Kitchener, who happened to be paying an imperial visit at the time, saw Ogilvie whisked back to London to advise the War Office. His ailerons, originally hung by piano hinges, reappeared on British designs. And we forgot about him.

Just staying with aviation for a moment, because it's an interesting example of how we take to a new technology, how many New Zealanders know that the first flying boat designed, built and flown in the southern hemisphere, was created in Auckland by pioneer flyer, Leo Walsh? Or that our own Herbert Pithers built the world's first all-metal monoplane.

As we brace ourselves for that millennial sunrise over Pitt Island or Mount Hikurangi or – for all I know – Dunsandel, we need to remind ourselves that nearly a hundred years ago, some of us at least were enthusiastically embracing the potential and promise of an unproven invention. And we're still doing it now. In a world where information technology is overcoming the tyranny of distance, Wellington is the most wired city on the planet. We obviously like being trailblazers, adapters, consumers of the new. None of this should come as any surprise. At a time when we seem determined to exaggerate and exacerbate our differences, perhaps we need to remind ourselves that we have this, at least, in common. We are all the sons and daughters of explorers, descendants of people who swapped the known for the unknown, willing to risk the peril to taste the promise.

Given that background, given that we can point to a tradition of specific achievements, innovations and inventions that's still going strong, we should be feeling quite cheerful, optimistic even. We should be celebrating our inventors. We should be rejoicing the fact that, in the sporting arena, we can claim 42 world champions. Yet, I suspect we'd be struggling to name more than six. Why is this? Why do inventors distrust someone who contacts them with a view to telling their story? Why do we doubt our ability to come up with ideas that match or surpass those produced overseas, when the evidence that we can is in your hands?

Increasingly, and sadly, I think it's because we're accepting a false view of the world. I find it ever more difficult to tolerate the superficial partiality of much New Zealand journalism. It's not just that there are too many journalists trying to win the election without standing for Parliament. That's bad enough, but worse is the slavish addiction to the dysfunctional. We seem to be trapped in a truly vicious circle, caught in a culture of denigration, where anything goes so long as it's lurid. Real or imagined scandals and shocks are the daily norm and those who stand to gain from such allegations – and there always are those who stand to gain – appear to have willing and credulous allies: the

Kelly's tube valve amplifier

media, people who assume a scandal claimed is a scandal proved. And that their job is simply to trumpet the charge. Well, it's good copy I guess, and it's easier than applying a critical intelligence. But what bothers me is that I think it's having a significant and corrosive effect on the way we see ourselves. It would be overstating the case to say that success is the new obscenity, but we do seem to be remorselessly determined to focus on failure.

I simply say that that's not factual. And that it's not necessary to create a Pollyanna world of ersatz good news to achieve a balance. Just a willingness to tell all the stories, to understand that we have more than a political tradition and that merely because it's harder to find an inventor in a shed than an M.P. in the House who's willing to whinge, doesn't mean that somebody shouldn't be making the effort.

The inventors in this book speak for themselves. But they do tell us something about New Zealand as well. It's something we should enjoy. And, yes, something we should celebrate. Without apology. I hope the inventors feel good about the book. The rest of the world sees it. As one visitor from abroad put it not so long ago, 'You New Zealanders – if you can't buy something, you invent it.' And more often than not in the shed, where everything began. I hope it gets a few people thinking about effective ways to overcome some of the obstacles that can get in the way of a good idea. I hope we can reduce the paranoia and release the potential. I hope you get a buzz out of seeing some of the things other people have created. Some of them will succeed, some of them probably won't, even though they deserve to. But the inventors will keep going anyway. It's what they do. Or put another way, and in another's words, 'To do this you need huge balls and a very poor perception of failure.'

Don's sheep cradle

Kevin

Tough, light and ready to roll

Were we to issue durable clipboards and reliable biros to some of those little men in white coats who so energetically police A & P shows, and then send them forth to conduct a nationwide towbar count, it would be possible to confirm what for now can only be an educated guess. Namely, that the incidence of towbars, and by inference trailers, is higher here than anywhere else in the civilised world. Which excludes Australia, otherwise it might be a contender.

But be that as it may, overseas travel does reveal a relative paucity of trailers in parts abroad. Not so here. We love them. So it should come as no surprise that one sheddie's invented a trailer for the 21st century. There's no doubt the Tuff Lite is Kevin Roman's pride and joy. He's designed it himself, built it himself and he's definitely serious about seeing it succeed. If there's any aspect of trailer operation or potential that he's overlooked, it's not immediately obvious.

To begin with, the Tuff Lite is made of 'indestructible' polyethylene. 'You could run a car into the side of it and it'd bounce off,' says Kevin. Should you need to you could load it up with a tonne of material and it would still float over rivers. There's a lightweight top that can be removed by one person and which, when raised, allows loading from three sides. If your trailer only comes out in summer you could use it as a giant compost bin for six months of the year, then hose it out and go camping. It comes with a roof rack, front storage compartment and body mouldings that can serve as fuel or water tanks in areas like outback Australia and South Africa. Users closer to home have been considered as well. Commercial operators will be able to load 1200 by 2400 (8 by 4) timber planks and similar large loads.

Such a package will be 'more expensive than an open trailer', concedes Kevin. But it will be 'very comparable with a shuttle trailer — the ones you see at airports. Only you'll get more volume in this.' To make it in New Zealand will mean a retail price around $4,500 or 'if it's made in Pakistan or somewhere we could import it and sell at about the $3,000 mark.'

Then again, you could leave your funds under the mattress and wait for the Stage 2 version. Because that will add a pontoon-style 3.5-metre polyethylene boat to Kevin's invention. Looking like a rigid IRB the boat will feature an underfloor fuel tank and drop-in seats that double as storage containers. A keen camper and boatie himself, Kevin initially thought he 'could make a trailer with a top that would be a boat'. But he 'couldn't make it work without compromising either one'.

Using his pattern making skills, Kevin's produced a model of Stage 2 and 3. The boat fits over the trailer roof.

Kevin Roman and the first-ever Tuff Lite, which was built in Kevin's shed before he sold the house.

The solution was a boat that will fit on the existing trailer with no modifications. 'This is the ultimate package. When you're out fishing you can leave all your gear still locked up in the trailer.' And if that takes your fancy, so will Stage 3. This will see four modular sections — a front, two sides and a rear — that can be dropped into place on the sides of the trailer to turn it into a camper once the roof's back on. So far Stage 2 (the boat) and Stage 3 (the extensions) only exist in model form, but Kevin estimates the boat will cost an extra $2,500 and the camper walls about $850. Add everything up, he says, and you've got a New Zealand-made trailer, boat and mobile home for about $8,000 — or less, obviously, if it was built offshore.

How to make your trailer your bedroom.

Concerned with growing, not going, the Propagro is Kevin's first invention. The secret here is the manufacturing, he explains. 'This is the only propagator that's vacuum-formed and injection-moulded. So this is half the price of the others and just as good — or even better. Because the others have their vents on top, but the optimum place is the sides. Having them there retains the moisture and keeps things more humid.'

But ultimately, where the plant goes is a secondary issue. Kevin's primary and unswerving goal is just to get the trailer built. Like Tim Shadbolt, he really doesn't care where. 'This is my whole life. I sold my house to put money into the trailer,' he says, adding ruefully, 'it's all gone now. It's amazing how much money these things gobble up.' Fortunately, he can use the skills he's acquired over fourteen years as a pattern maker to bring extra funds in. 'I'm still working for other people,' he says. 'I can't knock that off yet. But the day will come . . .' Kevin rests an arm on the prototype ' . . . this trailer is going to work.'

Kevin has long-term plans for tandem and tipper versions of the trailer. A key benefit of every variant is that they'll be virtually maintenance-free. The only bits that will need replacement are the tyres and wheel bearings, says the inventor.

Fitted with tiller steering and a surplus motorbike engine, the old three-wheeler could get two blokes (Gordon and his son Keith), one dog and a couple of sickly sheep over the toughest terrain.

Unlikely as it may seem, Gordon insists his scaffolding system works. When you're painting the house, he says, your weight keeps the system stable. The upper arms are fitted with lateral bars to eliminate rocking or movement of tiles.

Gordon

Thinking on his farm

Should you happen to have a haphazard hedge in need of a trim, Gordon's gear can cut it. Should you chance to own a sawdust stack that's got to be nicely dry, Gordon's sorted that out. Should you face the fact your scaffolding's nicked right when the house needs painting, Gordon's got it covered. Should you choose to keep a flock of sheep and don't know how to load them, Gordon's found an answer. Several answers, in fact, as this paragraph would suggest. But mate, there's more!

Here's a man who's always loved solving problems. Over the years, Gordon's consistently held the view, Why buy it when you can build it? Because he's had to, but also because he enjoys the challenge. If, as he's quick to concede, 'the mother of invention is necessity' then the father has been his own tireless ingenuity.

A visit to his farm quickly proves the point. It's strewn with evidence of his inventive impulse. Gordon Fergusson came here as a 22-year-old in 1946 and has been working the land ever since. His father was 'always tinkering with various little gadgets' he says, and he's maintained the tradition. 'I've always looked at ways of doing things easier or cheaper. I've always looked for a different angle.'

An early example of this lateral tendency, the 'original three-wheeler' he built 35 years ago, is still in the shed. 'It was very novel, the only thing around here that would go over really rough or steep ground. Our winters get very, very wet and if a sheep was in trouble, you couldn't get to it.' That was the spur to build it, 'way before today's three-wheelers and farm bikes' and it worked. Equally effective is the vertical mower that's been trimming his hedges and the ones round the local school for a good many years. Heath Robinson would approve of this one, which is designed to go on the front of a tractor. Gordon's mounted a standard lawn mower side-on at the top of an 6-metre pole. About two-thirds of the way down the pole, there's a curved bar and counterweight, so the rig can be guided to cut great sweeping swathes through the rampant foliage.

Another aerial aid is the hanging scaffolding he invented after coming under pressure to get the house painted. Not your ordinary scaffolding this, it actually hangs from the roof, with the planks sitting on top of the lower horizontal arms. 'Definitely for single-storey houses only,' says Gordon, acknowledging that in this day and age, 'OSH would frown very much on that.'

But probably not on the sheep loader. It's a straightforward race hooked up to an old washing machine motor, giving him the ability to raise and lower the ovine equivalent of an air bridge. Another item that Gordon's found indispensable is his sawdust drier. After diversifying into export bulbs, he hit a snag. 'You can't buy dry sawdust.' Yet he needs it. If the sawdust's too wet, it rots his harvest. If it's desert-dry, it sucks essential moisture from the bulbs. So Gordon produced a solution. Some surplus 40-gallon drums connected like a

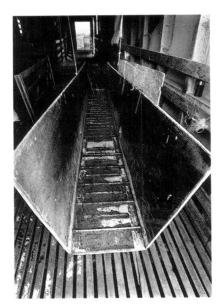

The sheep loader's proved extremely popular with truckies. 'They love it,' says Gordon. 'A lot of trucks now have three decks and with this you can reach any deck you want.' The loader's driven by an old washing machine motor with the agitator acting as the winch.

long tin snake to an old concrete mixer. 'You just put the sawdust in the high end,' he explains, 'and it tumbles down dry.'

Like most of his inventions, the drier is the essence of effective simplicity, a perfect marriage of what's needed and what's available. Gordon gets real satisfaction from that and from the possibility that his ideas might be of practical value to other people. 'Different guys would be able to knock that up no trouble at all,' he says pointing to the drums. 'How many would want to build a sawdust drier is another thing. There could be only half a dozen throughout the universe. But if it's any help, good luck to them.'

The sawdust drier puts the circular action of an old concrete mixer to good use. The drums are painted black to absorb the heat and assist the drying process. 'They get so hot you can't put your hands on them,' says Gordon.

Another of Gordon's home-built inventions is this self-tipping trailer. The mudguards used to be part of a wringer washer, the axle came from a Mini. Two Big Fork rams provide the drive-on, drive-off tipping mechanism.

Colin

Getting back to work

Colin Gans: more people should take things lying down.

Picking up a kayak the wrong way has had some pretty serious repercussions for Colin. Born in South Africa, he came to New Zealand eleven years ago to study information sciences at Otago University. If that sounds somewhat sedentary, his relaxation was anything but. 'I've done a lot of extreme sports over the years, I was really into them.' All that changed about two years ago, on a sea kayaking expedition. 'I went to pick up one of the boats . . . and I just must've lifted it the wrong way.'

The result was a disabling prolapsed disc. Not only was extreme sport out of the question, his ability to earn a living was suddenly in doubt. He knew he needed an operation on his back. What he didn't need, and couldn't afford, was the three-month enforced lay-off that would follow the surgery. A self-employed database consultant, Colin knew he needed an alternative desk. Something that would allow him to work in a prone position.

So he built one. 'I made the first prototype in the shed and it's just evolved through a series of modifications. I started out with a standard typing trolley but its come a long way since then.' Far enough to get a patent and a name — the FLOWstation — a shortened version of the original title, Flat Out Work Station. With an early version installed, Colin was back at work three days after his operation. And although he's recovering from the injury, he remains dependent on the system. 'I find it uncomfortable to sit for any length of time, so I use it then. And if I've got stressful work to do, I do that on it as well. It's a very relaxed way of working.'

Assembling a FLOWstation is a job 'best done by two people', says Colin, with the final height adjustments 'preferably done by someone without a back problem'. Installation takes 'less than five minutes' and the $1,000 kit comes complete with mouse and keyboard, chiefly because 'you may have difficulty finding a keyboard that would match'. Colin doesn't think the local market's big enough to guarantee success for his invention. 'If it's going to really take off, I must get it into the United States.' To help with that, although it's not his core business, he's marketing the FLOWstation on the Internet. 'I don't think it will make me buckets of money. But if it helps people in a similar situation to myself I'm happy. I've enjoyed it all. It's been a really interesting experience.'

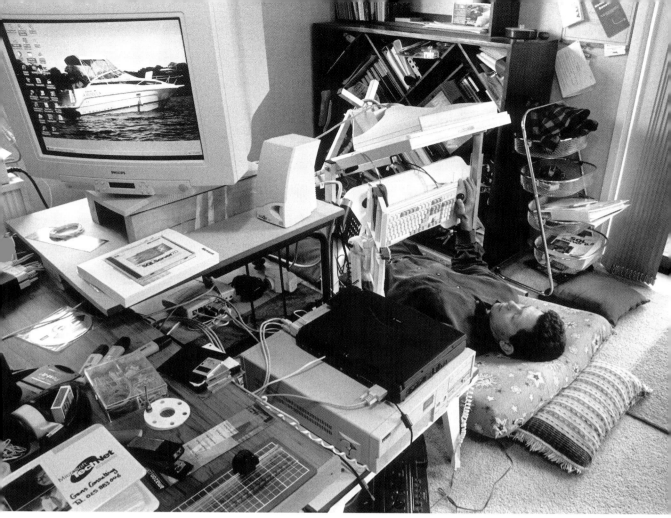

Benefits of the FLOWstation, says Colin, include reducing neck pain, allowing overuse injuries to heal, and a better focus on critical tasks. He's also designed a version that can be used over a bed.

The keyboard's easily secured with Velcro and the trackball mouse doesn't rely on gravity to work.

What happens when the rake's stood on. The angled head keeps the handle well away from the treadee's visage.

Ray
600 and still counting

Should the Governer General, or his republican successor, ever feel inclined to bestow an award for ingenuity — let's say the OBI (Order of Brilliant Ingenuity) — then Ray Fox would be right up there as a worthy recipient of the gong. Here's a gent who's already got more than 600 reasons to claim the title, 'Our Most Inventive Bloke'. That's the number of ideas and inventions Ray's got on file so far. And he shows no sign of quitting, slowing down or giving up. Some of his ideas are grand and, it must be said, untested. One such example is his plan to have us drive on talking roads. Embodying, as he says, 'the right mixture of craziness and possibility', the proposal is to engineer a road's surface in a way that mimics the grooves on a long-playing record. Whizzing over these grooves, one's tyres would act 'like a needle and speak to you', relaying helpful advice concerning speed limits, dangerous bends and the like. And, if the Roadaphone seems fantastical, try one of Ray's more whimsical wheezes — the half-umbrella that allows lovers to stay cheek to cheek in the rain.

Working on the computer in his shed, he produces a regular newsletter full of such notions. They're all 'copyleft', that's to say, 'left around to be copied'. As are the elaborate and often outlandish inventions of one Professor Karakapotu, a researcher very well known to Ray and the creator, amongst other things, of Instant Dirt, 'the spray-on dirt for all occasions'. A quick squirt will make the average home look suitably scruffy, so that unwelcome relatives are persuaded not to stay too long. Or if they do stay, they'll be so busy cleaning up they won't waste time with idle chit-chat.

But it would be misleading to suggest that Ray's just an inventor with his tongue in his cheek. He's come up with a host of other ideas that are both novel and more serious. Among them, a fridge door tap to dispense iced water, a bounce-proof backpack, a glow-in-the-dark toilet seat, an add-on alarm that sounds when a hot tap's left running, a Leggo sorting bucket, in-bed exercise equipment, a TV violence tax (payable by the broadcaster), a pint-sized exercise pool fitted with an Archimedes screw that produces a constant current, so the fitness fanatic can simultaneously swim and stay in the same spot, a small unit to sterilise a toothbrush, an inflatable highchair and a totally rigid safety rake.

The rake is interesting for two reasons. First, because its angled head means that if you stand on the teeth, it is impossible 'to get hit in the face or puncture your foot'. And second because it enables Ray to make a bold claim. 'I'm a freak. I'm the only inventor in the whole wide world who has approached a possible user of an idea and sold it immediately. I'm the only one.' He's talking about the day he walked into the offices of a New Zealand manufacturer of garden tools and implements and asked what they thought of his prototype. 'They said it was the perfect safety rake and offered me $2,000 for it. I don't know anyone who's able to parallel that.' Sadly, another gardening invention — a kneeler that doubles as a seat — hasn't enjoyed equal success. 'It's a good

The rake that sold itself. With angled teeth designed to prevent injury, it not only rakes normally but will efficiently rake grass, rocks and stones as well as soil.

By gluing a strip of Velcro to a length of flexible hose, Ray's created a clip-on feature that makes a whiteboard pen its own duster.

These polystyrene LokBloks are an invention Ray came up with several years ago. Self-locking and requiring no skill to assemble or dismantle, they're intended for use in 'rebuildable walls and buildings'.

idea if you can make it for five dollars. But New Zealand manufacturers can't make it for forty dollars.'

In the last few years, Ray's abandoned the battle, sometimes successful, sometimes not, to get his inventions to the market. Not because he's lost his enthusiasm. As he says, 'At 83, you've got to have a zest for life or you wouldn't be round any more.' But if the mind is willing, the body's not so sure. He's been in and out of hospital having various parts of his 'worn-out machinery poked and prodded, being hauled back and forth to this or that high-tech scanner or analyser'. So he hasn't needed a talking road to tell him to slow down. The tools that used to be in his shed have gone, passed on to friends and grandchildren. These days, says Ray, 'If I can't make it with what I have on hand — masking tape and cardboard — I don't bother.'

These self-imposed limitations haven't stopped some ingenious ideas emerging. Such as his DIY dust collector, requiring no extra apparatus other than one shopping bag and a bulldog clip. It's a typical example, says Ray, 'of a non-commercial invention. The kind of thing that traps inventors. They spend years on non-commercial inventions then wonder why their family's gone.' Another invention he's not striving to market is his two-in-one whiteboard pen and duster. This simply adds a strip of hose and a piece of Velcro to the standard item so that you can write on and wipe off with the same implement. When he first produced the idea he 'tried to commercialise it', but at that stage he says, 'no one was interested', so he's stopped trying. He gets his satisfaction now from just throwing up new ideas, simple inventions, things that other people can adapt and use if they wish. His shed's his playground and he's more than happy to settle for having fun.

Back in the days when Ray was a teacher, he was also a writer. 'I used to write under a pseudonym, because teachers couldn't have a second job. When I retired from writing I switched from using words as my vehicle to invent with. I turned to other materials; wood, metal, paper, iron and steel. I just changed from words to more tangible territory. And that's what I've been doing ever since.'

Ray's DIY dust catcher. Two notches on the sides of a long-handled shovel allow a shopping bag to be hooked into place. The bag's then clipped to the handle as the dusting's done. A quick backwards tilt sends the dust into the bag which, when full, can be easily disposed of.

Andy

A measure of success

Before Andy Pang came here, he was a mechanic. That was in Hong Kong. Not a place renowned for its bungalows, as any Handycam-wielding tourist will confirm. There never were a lot of hipped roofs or timber tower blocks ten feet from the wing-tip on the way into Kai Tak. Like many, Andy remembers a concrete landscape stuccoed with people. 'In Hong Kong, there was no place to do anything. Your home was like a small garage.' Not any longer. For the last eight years, Andy's savoured two things he'd never had a lot of — space and time. 'Now we have leisure. And a bigger place. So I make a workshop and try to do something.'

What he did was change direction, taking an Institute of Technology carpentry course. Where he found he wasn't the only one bemused by the intricacies of roof construction. 'A roof has a lot of different angles,' he says. 'Many students felt it was very hard to work out the angles. So I designed a tool for them.' As ever, a few words describe a great deal of effort. Andy spent a lot of hours in the workshop he'd set up before the Pan-Cut finally emerged. Along the way, he realised he had something that could do more than unravel the mysteries of roofs. What started as a teaching aid could actually tackle thirty different jobs. The Pan-Cut will serve as an internal and external square, a bevel, a circular saw cutting guide, marking gauge, right and left-hand side protractor, spirit level and measuring device for common rafter plumb and seat cuts, hip valley and jack rafter cuts, purlin top edge and side cuts, stair rise and roof fall settings and tangents.

Perhaps it was inevitable, when Andy launched it in 1997, that there were those who had doubts. 'Pan-Cut looks . . . like a tool invented by a committee' was how one building mag saw it, adding, 'nothing quite like the device . . . has appeared anywhere before'. But looks aren't everything, as any gnarled chippie will tell you, and *Progressive Building* went on to discuss the 'claim to perform a total of 30 functions' before concluding 'careful analysis shows that Pan-Cut does them all, often with a functional advantage over traditional counterparts'.

Encouraged by the feedback, Andy approached one of his tutors to write an instruction booklet, and launched his tool of all trades onto the market. So far, sales have been 'OK, but not very fast'. Andy's sold more than 2000 and says, 'When you consider the small population, that's not too bad.' And could've been better. For a few glorious months, he thought he'd clinched a deal with an international manufacturer. There were meetings, discussions with senior executives, the prospect of promotions in the States. Then, suddenly, the bubble burst. The company told Andy, 'We can't sell it now.' He still doesn't know why. 'Maybe we were talking to the wrong guy' is as close to an explanation as he got.

Andy demonstrates how the Pan-Cut can help to raise the roof. The vertical and horizontal arms serve as metric and imperial rules, while the semi-circular centre section is marked to facilitate measurements for a wide range of cuts. The commercial version is manufactured in New Zealand and sells for $90.

The collapse of these negotiations has been a setback for a man whose hero is John Britten. 'I would like to be successful like him,' says Andy. But his definition of success is a demanding one. 'If we were in the United States, we could sell a million. That is my goal. If I sold a million, I would feel successful. But I don't feel successful because I have not done that.'

Till he does, he'll keep working as a builder to supplement his income. The Pan-Cut is his first invention, and putting it into production has been an expensive exercise. But he's learnt a lot as well as spent a lot and, for now, he's prepared to be patient. 'I think I'll wait until this is successful, then invent other products. It involves too much money to try to do too much at one time.'

With thirty functions, the Pan-Cut serves as a substitute for ten other tools. And that, says Andy, makes it exceedingly useful for professionals and home handymen alike.

Strictly for his own use so far, Andy may make this drawing board the subject of future development. Another multi-purpose design, it can be set at any height or angle, and positions the light box underneath to make the tracing of negatives easier.

Chris

Off to a flying start

Statistics may not have agreed with dear old Benjamin Disraeli. In fact, he found them so vexatious, he bequeathed us one of the most memorable quotes we have on the matter. 'There are three kinds of lies,' harrumphed the 19th-century prime minister, 'lies, damned lies and statistics.'

Others are more dispassionate. They take the view that, used in moderation, statistics can have the beneficial effect of giving precision to a hunch. That's why one statistic, in particular, makes Chris's eyes light up. 'Right now,' he says in an accent guaranteed to thrill Shirley Valentine, 'right now a billion people are moving as tourists around the globe.' This fact leads him to a conclusion. 'In the next century — and that's just tomorrow — tourism is going to be the biggest activity of human beings.' And the conclusion, in turn, gives rise to a prediction. 'As tourists get more and more jaded and blasé, tourism will become an event. *This* is an event.'

There would not be many sheds in New Zealand with their own wind tunnel. Chris Sacatos built his to test this design and other aeronautical innovations such as a radically different kite he's working on at present. He's always loved aircraft 'All my life. I love aircraft. During the war, in Egypt, I was mad about modelling, but you couldn't get balsa to build them. So we used to go to the RAF airfield and get balsa out of wrecked Mosquitos. I don't know how we got past the guards.'

This is the Hyperion — an 8.5-metre long, 2.5-metre high, 24-passenger, lifting-body tourist aircraft. For Chris, its first flight will be the fulfilment 'of the old dream of mankind to sit on a magic carpet and see everything'. Not as travellers do today. 'This will be the ultimate in comfort and silence. It will be strictly a caviar and champagne flight.' With passengers able to move about in an aircraft built to fly very slow and very low.

One of the reasons it can do this is its lifting-body design. Such designs do not rely solely on their wings to provide lift as most planes do. The fuselage or body is also shaped as an aerofoil to provide lift — hence the name. This idea isn't new. American aero-engineer Jack Burnelli produced lifting-body designs in the 1930s. So did the German aircraft manufacturer Junkers. As a boy, Chris remembers seeing a Junkers G38 airliner which carried twelve of its passengers within the wings. 'I saw it in Athens in 1938. It was great for its time. Bloody slow, but huge.'

That's something the Hyperion won't be. But it will be unique. Because Chris has literally invented a new way to fly. 'Every time an aircraft turns,' he explains, 'it has to bank. But this one must fly absolutely level in the turn. And I have succeeded in doing this in a special way.' In his shed under the house, Chris has designed, built and wind-tunnel-tested a completely new lift mechanism which eliminates the need for moving surfaces like flaps. The wing is very, very special. 'Fifty percent more efficient than usual,' he says. 'There is no such aircraft anywhere in the world.'

The job now is to build a radio-controlled model to prove the concept. Chris has sunk $5,000 of his own in the venture and got an additional $5,000 as a Business Development grant. Once the model's been tested, a single seat, 1/6-scale version of the Hyperion will take to the air. That'll cost $2 million. Then two full-size hulls, one to be tested to destruction. They'll cost $20 million. Then and only then the Hyperion will go into production. 'Each one,' says Chris, 'will cost $12 million US. Over the next twenty years, I expect to sell a thousand.'

The Hyperion has a distinguished pedigree. Four years ago, friends brought Chris plans for an inverted vee-tail lifting-body cargo aircraft designed by Bert Rutan, one of the world's most innovative aircraft designers. After years of study and computer simulations, the project had been abandoned, but Chris could see potential in the concept. The end result, redesigned, reconfigured for passenger use and with his own wing section and lift mechanism, is the Hyperion.

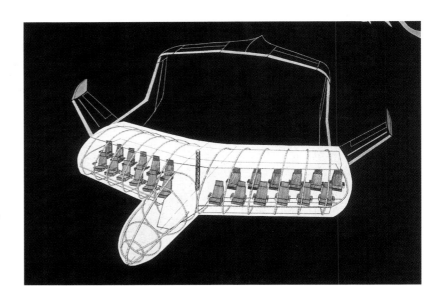

Don't shake your head. This man is serious. He's a qualified aircraft designer who's spent most of his working life in the aviation industry in America. With the Hyperion theoretically proven, and specifically geared to the burgeoning tourism market, Chris is convinced it's ideal for New Zealand. 'It's not a swing-wing supersonic fighter, or high-tech speedboat. This is a barge. It has minimal electronics, it's very low-tech. It'll be made in plastic materials . . . and we're the best in the world in plastic-hull construction. Plus, we have very good engineers, superb aeronautical engineers.'

In fact, he goes further. As an emigrant, someone who sees us through an outsider's eyes, Chris has a view that would see news editors jamming their fingers in their ears and running screaming in horror. 'This is the best country in the world to be in right now,' says this son of Greek parents who live in Egypt. 'It's a privilege to live in this country. We have our problems, who doesn't? But we seem to be getting along. There is nothing like a Kiwi . . . the people here are the best of all the countries I've been in. From the beginning of my time here, it's been my privilege to be involved with the black-singlet Kiwis. Once they call you mate, you know you are accepted. They'll do anything for you. They are the salt of the earth.'

The Hyperion cruising over a scenic vista. The plane 'has to be beautiful, it's an entertainment experience,' says Chris. In antiquity, Hyperion was the name of the Greek sun god. At the start of each day, Hyperion would guarantee light by pulling the sun from east to west in a chariot.

A former master jeweller, who did his training at Cartier in London, Ted was lured here by the open spaces shortly after the Second World War.

Two elastic straps, fitted with Velcro, hold the Xtend-a-Viza in place. It can be easily slipped down using one hand. Ted says the AA is interested in retailing the product through its stores.

Ted
Beating the glare

If attention to detail is the key to success, then Ted Gardiner has got it made. A quick glance at the Xtend-a-Viza shows something so obvious and so simple that it looks as if it could be knocked up in less time than it takes to explain the theory of relativity. But that's not the case.

Countless hours of meticulous analysis followed an idea born in an emergency. 'The road in front of our place runs east–west,' Ted explains. 'It goes up one side and down the other. One afternoon, I came over the hill and was completely blinded by the sun. There was a car parked out on the road and I almost hit it. My wife was really shaken up, so when we got inside, I thought I'd do something.'

What he did was make a rudimentary felt-on-cardboard prototype. 'To make that first one took six hours,' Ted says. 'To get to this stage has taken six years.' That's because very early on, he identified a problem. And an opportunity. 'I realised if I got a new car, I'd need a new visor. So I thought, if I made something that would fit all cars, I could sell them. And that's how it began.'

The search for a universal solution 'geared for all those people who are five foot eight and under' took him to car yards, new and used. Heaps of them. He's now on first name terms with most of the local salesmen. 'I sat in every car they had on all the lots to take measurements. I'd spend the whole day playing with figures, then I'd make a model. And if something wasn't right, I'd try again.'

Eventually he was satisfied his invention would fit the visors of just about every limo and landau on sale in the land. Except the $300,000-plus Lamborghini Countach which comes complete with a space-saving folding visor, so sadly if you drive one of those, you're out of luck. But everybody else is pretty much catered for. Ted's even got the aesthetics sorted. 'I've had to have elastic made . . . you can't buy grey elastic. People won't buy something that makes their car an eyesore.'

A burglary inspired Ted to invent his own home security system. He dug out his old jeweller's tools and made up a set of stainless steel clips to secure windows and doors. Easy to fit and hard to detect, Ted says the clips 'give you that extra peace of mind when you're away from the house'

Nor will they buy something that's not safe. 'I had all sorts of problems with that,' says Ted. 'The Land Transport Safety people wanted to test it to destruction. They told me they couldn't test it, so they gave me some addresses in Japan, the US and the UK. And somewhere in Australia as well. But they said I'd have to pay. So I spoke to one of the research agencies here that used to be part of the DSIR. They said bring it round and when they saw it they laughed. They said it doesn't need testing, but if it did we'd be the best people to do it. They'd just finished testing all the parts for the new frigates, for vibration and so on.'

On the basis of this curious encounter, there could well be a healthy market for anyone skilled enough to invent a form of common sense able to be successfully administered to land safety bureaucrats.

As for the future, the man who came here from the UK in 1957 is reasonably sanguine. Ted doesn't expect his invention to make a fortune. 'But it'd be nice if it gives us enough money for a good holiday once a year. The thing is, it's so simple. It's like the safety pin. But it really works.'

Paul

No danger to the endangered

When you've always been 'a bit of a recluse' and 'a bit of an inventor' and you 'come from quite a long line of commercial fishermen' then, like as not, at some stage you'd have the time and the inclination to do something to enhance the lot of those engaged in piscatorial practices. That's exactly what Paul Waghorn has done. Working in a shed that was originally built as an ablutions block, he's invented a better fish trap. It's always been assumed that inventing a better mouse trap would see the world beating a path to one's door. Whether the planetary turns up at Paul's place is a moot point. But them as wears waders are likely to turn up in reasonable numbers.

The great benefit of Paul's trap, other than being rustproof and not likely 'to bang your boat around', is that it can be safely used whenever and wherever there's a ban on set nets. It was, in fact, just such a set net ban in his area that started Paul thinking about alternatives. 'Set nets are pretty inefficient,' he says. 'They lose fish and undersize ones die. There's a lot of wastage with them, up to half the catch some days.' His trap overcomes those very real problems. Using it, Paul can 'target a species pretty exactly, through the choice of bait or where you put it. And anything you don't want, or that's undersize, you just release.'

There wouldn't be too many sheds like this. Originally built as the ablutions block when the old school became a youth hostel, this is now where Paul builds his traps.

Moreover, he notes, and this has aroused interest overseas, 'it's dolphin-friendly and penguin-friendly'.

Simplicity's another friendly aspect of Paul's traps. To build one he needs very little other than three pieces of polythene pipe, some nylon mesh and a generous helping of shingle. The pipes are hooped, but not before two have been filled with shingle. These become the base of the trap, ensuring it is 'heavy and won't move in the tides'. With mesh strung between this weighted base and the third hoop, the trap's virtually complete. 'The shingle in the bottom pipes and air in the top keeps it steady,' says Paul. 'You don't need a big buoy.' Just the right bait, hung from the top, and easy, swim-in access for the finned feeders. That's taken care of in one version with two entrances, and the other with four.

Paul's had as many as nine fish in them. 'Some days, other guys have been fishing with lines and catching nothing. But I've caught fish with them.' The traps have no rigid vertical elements, so they're collapsible. 'Just chuck 'em in the boot,' the inventor says, 'and you're off. They don't rust away, or bang your boat around. They're easy to retrieve and you can run over them with your car and they won't get damaged.'

So far the assembly line's not exactly humming. 'I'm selling to friends and acquaintances mainly,' says Paul. 'I sold about seven at the market day. For the first day out, that's quite good.' But, despite the relatively slow start, he enjoys making them and has patented the trap. He would consider full production, especially if there's a good reaction overseas. The traps have aroused interest in Australia, in particular from the Melbourne area, where there's a growing demand for fresh fish and 'the only way you can catch them is in traps'. He's already started to design a craypot, employing the same principle but with escape apertures to give undersize cray a way out.

Content with a quiet and solitary life in what was once a youth hostel, and before that a one-roomed school, Paul's always liked to tinker with new ideas. Sometimes there's been more tinkering than development. 'Lots of things I've tried haven't worked. But the trap seemed to work straight off. That's been the biggest buzz for me, having it work.'

The eco-trap as it would look on the sea bed. Although it's designed 'for recreational fishermen more than the commercial', Paul can't see any reason why much larger versions couldn't be produced for those who fish for a living.

Geoff in his inventers den. The Edison jukebox is on the right, and the Catchwave radio booster sits atop it. Designed to be used indoors, the Catchwave reduces static, fading and interference. To boost a favourite programme, place the radio on the crossmember at the base of the antenna and it enhances frequencies between 531 and 1602 on the AM band. The Catchwave is designed to pack flat for travellers and holidaymakers.

Geoff

Catching flies and making waves

Few would dispute the assertion that one of the goals of any invention is to put a bob or two in the pocket of its creator. So it is ironic in the extreme that Geoff Fergusson can claim the rare distinction of inventing something so good he can't sell it. Mind you, the briefest glimpse of his truly sublime fly catcher explains why he's in that unenviable position. It seems particularly unfair, given that he's actually found a sensible use for those wretched plastic excrescences in which assorted sarsaparillas and carbonated waters are sold by the trillion.

The irony's not lost on the inventor. 'I suppose it's the ultimate DIY invention really. It was a bit of a humanitarian effort — something for everyone. I took it to Mystery Creek for a laugh,' Geoff admits, 'but it won a prize. An awful lot of farmers are using it. It's simple to make, can adapt to any kind of bottle and it works really well. I've had inquiries from as far afield as the US.' He concedes it's a gesture as much as anything, but Geoff does sell an information pack covering construction, baits and related matters 'for the nominal fee of $5.90, to cover costs'.

Nor is his fly trap the only one that's got away. In the early 1970s, another great idea seized him. 'It really was a case of "Eureka" at 2 a.m.' He'd been wrestling, unsuccessfully, with the problem of how to stop the predations of certain plant pests. Until that early morning realisation that he could harness the attraction of colour. He'd invented the world's first photochromic lure. That was a simple idea too, a small flapping strip with 'no lure but colour' says Geoff. 'You just dipped it in any sticky medium, like oil.'

The idea's 'gone all around the world' but that hasn't helped Geoff. 'At the time I was really cheesed off with the lack of support. It could've been a New Zealand business that got it off the ground around the world . . . I didn't have the money to develop it myself. I didn't even have the money to patent it.'

Other inventions have enjoyed more success, among them two quiz boards, each with self-cancelling buzzers. One poses a series of questions related to New Zealand geography, while the other — the Quiz Whiz — is more general and has been popular with schools. The Catchwave AM signal enhancer, which his brother Allister also worked on, has had reasonable sales, although Geoff says the boom time was when Radio Pacific could not be picked up clearly in centres outside Auckland. 'It met a need,' he says, 'then that need was gone. But it's still ticking over.' Undeterred by the vicissitudes of the inventing life, Geoff continues to develop 'an assorted collection of gizmos and whizmos'. In his basement shed he's built a unique jukebox. 'It's the only one in the world,' says Geoff. Fully automated, it works as all jukeboxes do, except 'when you push the button you hear an old Edison phonograph cylinder play. There are other inventions too, but I can't show them. They're still under development.' One is an idea to improve efficiency in courtrooms which, surprisingly, given the goal, will retain lawyers. And there's 'a device to reduce wind-assisted accidents'.

However they perform commercially, Geoff can't see himself stopping. 'Why do I keep on? Sometimes I wonder. Inventing can be a very fraught business. But I like the quest for something new, being right out there on the edge of discovery and coming up with something nobody else has been able to do.' If only others could see the potential. 'I don't like the government funding approach necessarily. Sadly, a pool of money is needed for start-up funds. The frustrating thing is businesses could tap into enormous productivity and wealth if they'd just get behind certain good ideas . . . because we've got the people here who can come up with the good ideas.'

The DIY fly trap. As well as helping to reduce the multi-million dollar cost of flystrike in New Zealand, Geoff sees it as ideal for use in poorer countries for fly-borne disease control. Provided you've already bought the soft drink, the trap costs nothing, recycles plastic waste and takes 90 seconds to make.

Ken

A highlight for riders

Motorbikes always have been a seductive mode of transport. Traditionally cheaper than cars, they have a stimulating tendency to go like stink as well. The combination of these two factors has, over the years, drawn the red-blooded to them in large numbers. Amongst those lured by the appeal of the two-wheeler was Aircraftsman A.E. Shaw, better known as T.E. Lawrence, better known as Lawrence of Arabia. He could very well be the 20th century's pre-eminent motorbike fan. At something of a loose end once he'd finished hurtling about the Sahara doing untold mischief to the enemies of the Empire, he would ride flat out for miles on his bike, heedless of risk. His journals describe his addiction to speed, to the incomparable exhilaration it gave him. But in the end, it took much more. He lost his life in an accident, out riding his beloved bike.

The risks for a motorcyclist today are even greater. The machines are more powerful, the roads more crowded. Quite apart from the hazards of speed, there's the proven danger of reduced visibility. It's a problem on the open road and on crowded streets where traffic's constantly starting and stopping. As Ken Arnold points out, 'For motorcyclists, the brakes are down low and, depending on the length of the bonnet, drivers don't always see the light. A lot of people get killed, especially pillion riders on bikes. Cars go straight into the back of bikes, because they didn't see them stop.'

Big and bulky is how Ken describes his first-ever helmet-mounted light. 'It worked but it was clumsy.' It's since been refined. Ken's also designed a version for cycle helmets. 'I've fitted microswitches to the brake levers, front and back. A manufacturer could easily add them to the levers or cables.' The microswitches activate the transmitter, and the light comes on, just as it does on a motorbike. His cycle version, like the cheaper of the two available for motorbikes, would be externally mounted and secured with double-sided tape.

Ken's found a way to change that. He's invented something that gives motorcyclists the chance to use their heads. And their helmets. He's designed a built-in helmet light. 'You start the bike, turn on the key, and every time you touch the brakes, the light comes on.' The system mirrors the way a car's brake lights operate, except that Ken's done it remotely and not through a wiring system. His head light employs 'a wee transmitter mounted on the bike, under the seat and linked to the brake light. When that goes on the transmitter sends a signal to the helmet, and that lights up as well.' The transmitter, Ken says, is easy to install. 'It could be done by an auto-electrician or handyman.'

His first experiment was an externally mounted light, simply but effectively attached to the helmet with double-sided tape. He's gone on to produce a smaller and neater externally mounted version. Then there's the second generation light; his 'deluxe model' is actually built into the helmet. There's not one light but five, although there may be less on the production unit. Standard watch batteries provide power for the lights and Ken's already got test helmets 'on the road'. Reaction's been positive, he says. Some people 'don't understand the concept, but a lot think it's a great idea, a bit of ingenuity'.

That ingenuity is set to make its first commercial appearance overseas. 'It's actually being manufactured in China,' he says. 'There's too much red tape in this country.' He also thinks the first sales will be in China and Japan, where by law you now have to wear helmets on bikes and mopeds. He's already getting inquiries from motorcycle clubs in this country asking when it will be on sale. 'But they'll just have to wait a bit. Rome wasn't built in a day. When you're piddling round on your own it takes a lot of time — and money.'

Now that he's finally got something workable, buildable and saleable, Ken acknowledges it could make him rich. 'But I'm more interested in the safety of people on bikes. If you can eliminate some of those deaths, that's great. But you never know: the bloke who invented the stop light in the rear window of a car started off with something that was voluntary. Now it's compulsory. In ten years time, maybe all helmets will have to have them. At least I'll know it's saving lives. It's a great safety feature. I feel very comfortable wearing mine.'

Nothing to do with the highway, this is Ken's contribution to the warm way. He's called it the Hotty Top Off. He was inspired to invent it when he saw elderly people struggling with hot water bottles. 'I thought, there must be an easier way than this. It was just one of those things that comes into your mind.' He's had 4000 made and says, 'They sold well at Christmas. A lot of children bought them for their grandparents.' The next production run, he says, will be luminous, 'so people can find them at night'.

An easy rider, Ken says the helmet suits his style perfectly. 'I like to look at the scenery. I'm not into all that head-down, looking-at-the-white-line-all-the-time-stuff.'

Graeme

Bugs in the water

White water's always been one of nature's magnets. Maybe not for the aging and sedentary, but certainly for generations of ragged urchins devoted to the serious business of having fun. There wouldn't be too many Kiwis who haven't made at least one trip down a frothing, foaming river in an old tyre tube. And there's plenty like Graeme who have made a lot more than one. What sets him apart is that he did some thinking while he was floating. 'Twenty years ago, going down rivers, my brain began ticking over. I started thinking about how to improve the basic tyre tube.'

Two decades later, he's got the answer, the high-tech tube he's called the River Bug. In fact, getting the answer wasn't too hard. 'I thought it would be just a matter of coming up with a good idea, selling it off and getting on with the next one. What I've found is that coming up with the good idea is the easy bit. Making money out of it is very hard.' That hasn't deterred him yet. His wife Lindy works full time, allowing Graeme to devote time to developing and marketing the Bug, as well as 'playing around with ideas and doing a bit of house-husbanding'.

That doesn't leave him a lot of time to just get out and enjoy his invention. But he's done enough to confidently describe River Bugging as 'a cross between canoeing, body-boarding and rafting. They're great for running steep rivers with a current. It's like being in an escalator. You just lie back and manoeuvre from time to time.' Other Buggers agree. One veteran points out: 'There's an element of risk with kayaks. It's hard to get children interested. The real advantage of these is that you can use them without experience. They're a real fun machine, from my point of view and from a family point of view. You just put people in them and use them straightaway. You can go on Grade 2 or 3 water with no experience at all. If you tip over, you just pull the quick-release buckle and you're free.'

It's axiomatic that getting something to be that easy took a lot of effort. Like many other inventions, the River Bug's gone through numerous evolutions. 'It took about a year to get something that had the concept right,' says Graeme. 'By the time I'd done four prototypes, I had it right. With the sixth one, I'd got to the stage where I had a small production run done on it.' And people were impressed. 'It got a great reaction. People loved it. They wanted to know when I was going to make one for kids.' He says the shape is really the secret. 'With the float down each side, they're very stable. And light — we've done alpine crossings with them.' Not surprisingly, when a Bug weighs no more than 7 kg and, rather than needing a roof rack or special trailer, can 'be taken into remote rivers in a backpack'. Or be used as a pack itself, with room in the headrest for items like a sleeping bag or food, providing they're kept waterproof.

If you're wondering, then, why they aren't selling like hot kayaks (pardon the pun) it's because Graeme's confronted with a sizeable dilemma. 'We were idealistic at first; we wanted to get it Kiwi-made. It'd be nice to have it made in New Zealand, but it's just not possible. I could get them nearly as well-made in

Graeme Boddy: a good keen man with a new take on the tyre tube.

Korea, say, for a third of the price. There are factories there doing big military orders. It's nothing for them to flick over and do a small order like this.' But there's a catch. 'I could have them manufactured in Taiwan or Korea, but to get a thousand made, I'd have to throw $100,000 at it.

So, for now he's off on a different tack, opting to supply his Bugs only to adventure tourism and rafting companies. 'I'm really selling a new activity. That's working well. Young people like doing their own thing, not being told. This way, after a two-minute lecture, they can do it for themselves.' Using heavy-duty materials for those commercial versions, Graeme's making most of the components in his own shed, although the hulls are manufactured elsewhere. His ultimate plan is still 'to build a cheaper model for families', but that may take some time. The Bug's certainly not a financial success yet. 'There's still quite a good chance it could fall over, if it's not pushed the right way by the right people. It'll be really satisfying if they prove to be a financial success. And they're starting to gather momentum, to be a success, but there's a long way to go. They're still taking money from me, rather than giving it back.'

Just 1.6 m long, the River Bug has four major components: the hull, support, pillow and seat back. Portability is a big plus. Dismantled, the Bug can be packed for easy transport. A cheap hand pump is the ideal way to inflate the floats.

Bugs in use. Graeme knows that the actual invention is only one part of the story. 'Even if you've got a good product, you've got to use it the right way or it won't succeed.'

Ian Trafford

Noel
A wheelie good idea

You can't miss them really. They're all over New Zealand these days. Those large green plastic sentinels, standing in erratic ranks on the curb, waiting for the dustmen. For some they're a vile symbol of our addiction to waste. But for others, the wheelie bin is a handy, easy, efficient way to dispose of the mess. Certainly, for anyone with a bad back or dicky knee, or other frailty or affliction, they're easier to manage than the average well-filled bag or tin.

But sometimes, even a wheelie bin can be too heavy to handle. Especially when it has to traverse a long, steep, windy, uneven driveway. The kind that Noel S. Walker has, in other words. Five years ago, that driveway became an even bigger challenge for Noel. A serious stroke left him, at the age of 73, with limited mobility and strength. Suddenly, getting the rubbish out was a job he didn't relish at all.

So Noel set out to devise a way to make the difficult easy, and what he produced was the Binto. It's a nifty little idea. To make it work, all you need is a car with a towbar. The tube drops over the tow-ball, is secured by a thumb screw, and the wheelie bin handle drops into the slot at the top. From there, it's merely a matter of driving it to its appointed spot on the roadside and back again once it's been emptied. Not in reverse, though, says Noel. The car does need to be pointed in the direction you wish your bin to go.

With 250,000 wheelie bins in Auckland alone, Noel figures there's a good market for the product. It's ideal for people living up or down a long drive or anybody whose mobility is impaired by age or disability. Designing and making the prototype was something that gave him a lot of satisfaction as he recuperated. 'It was a matter of doing something,' he says, 'making it tick over a bit. I made the prototype up myself — buggered about with that for a long time. It was nine months in the making, actually.'

The Binto was patented last December and this year Noel's put his own money into an initial production run. He says he wishes he'd had the idea 'when wheelie bins were first introduced, but with more and more houses going on sections that, once upon a time, you couldn't build on, I hope the demand will still be there.'

On the wall in his study, behind the desk at which he does initial metalwork, there's a sign that reads, 'If you can afford to travel first class and don't — your heirs will.' That's clearly not a prospect Noel relishes. So, if the Binto takes off, the chances are that he will be doing so as well.

Noel with two early versions of the Binto in front of him on the bench.

The Binto tube in place on Noel's towbar. The retail price of the locally manufactured product is $18.00. The wheelie bin handle fits easily into the top slot. A notch prevents it from jumping out. And, because of the angle at which the bin sits, Noel says there's no problem with the lid coming open and spilling the contents.

Greg

Universities do some odd things. Entirely divorced from reality, they still assert a divine right to define it for the rest of us. To do this, they have an energetic tendency to establish entire departments of '-ologists', whose sole purpose in life is to hoover money from the pockets of taxpayers and students so they can state the screamingly obvious in words of a hundred syllables.

But every so often, the dreaming aspirers do something sensible. Take a recent study by a team of ovine investigators at Otago University, who set out to examine the physical effects of shearing 300 Southland ewes over an eight-hour period. They found that the effort involved in that is the same as would be required to move 5 tonnes for 5 kilometres. Put another way, it's the equivalent of running a marathon in the morning, then another in the afternoon.

Little wonder, then, that Greg Moffat says, 'If you took the emotion out of shearing, there'd be one of these in every shed.' But there's not. Far from it. For a very simple reason, in Greg's view. 'You wouldn't believe the number of cockies who're committed to the whole macho thing of bending over and stuffing

The inventor's lair. Not only did Greg design and build the shearing table prototype, but for years he manufactured them as well. 'I tried to get others to manufacture them, but it cost too much and took too long. The first thirty tables I had fabricated were fine, but with the last twenty, nothing would fit.' With an urgent Australian order to meet he had to put things right himself.

up their backs.' Clearly he isn't happy. And he's happy to say so. Even though the welfare of his spine wasn't the thing that led him to invent the Moffat Shearing Table some twenty-odd years ago.

'I invented this because I needed it. I had to have bread for breakfast.' He'd just bought a farm. 'But I couldn't shear. I'd do four and I was stuffed. In fact, the most I've ever done on the floor was forty a day. With this I can do two hundred and fifty.' Not quite as many as the professionals who, these days, average around 300, but more than enough for Greg, facing tight times on the farm. 'I used to be able to do a sheep in forty-five to fifty seconds. That's actual shearing time. We were doing a thousand a week, and saving $1,000. That was our grocery bill for three months.'

The table allows 'any person of normal motor control to safely shear sheep'. Indeed, Greg remembers when Pinetree Meads and a group of IHC kids came to see him. 'These kids watched me shear a couple of sheep, then they started asking if they could have a go. There was this fifteen-year-old boy, he never said a word, but he'd decided to try it. We put a sheep on the table and he shore the whole thing absolutely perfect.' To prove how easy it was, Greg would demonstrate the table at Field Days in a shirt, waistcoat and cloth cap.

The strategy's paid off. Over the past ten years, Greg's sold about 600, mostly to local farmers, but also overseas. 'When I was getting started, the biggest friend the farmer-inventor had was the *Journal of Agriculture*. It's gone now, but they used to send a thousand copies overseas, so the advertising went everywhere. That international exposure has led to sales in Zimbabwe, Spain, Canada, France, South Africa, Mexico, the United States, the United Kingdom,

The first-ever shearing table was invented in Australia in the 1890s. But Greg's is the only one to feature a 'tilt, swivel, roller combination' which enables it to be used not only for shearing, but also for footwork, mouthing, vaccination and animal husbandry.

Australia and King Island in the Bass Strait. In New Zealand, Greg sold his shearing table for $2,500, and he's quick to compare that with the cost of contract shearing which, he says, can be up to $3 per sheep. 'With this I'd say you could shear 2500 sheep in a month. There isn't one other piece of capital equipment on a farm that doesn't wear out and pays for itself in a month.'

Last year, Greg sold his patents for the shearing table to a New Zealand agricultural body. He's now toying with other ideas, including his own version of an automatic gate opener. But if the inventions are new, the approach is not. 'My basic principle when you're inventing something is to go back to when granddad was around. They didn't have the portability of power that we have. So you forget about motors, hydraulics, pneumatics and so on. And think about the weight you've got yourself or through the animal, and harness that.' As efficiently and inexpensively as possible, he says, because 'when you're inventing something for farmers it's got to be cheap — 78 percent of them are going to be in the red this year, so you've got to keep it simple and keep the costs down.'

Pursuing these goals has occasionally taxed the abundant patience of the wife. Greg admits there've been plenty of times when he's woken her up in the middle of the night with some new idea. 'Or got her to take notes while I was in the shower. She's been great.' He also values that strange and slightly surreal state of mind that sometimes comes just before you go to sleep. 'If you've got a technical problem, you set your mind to it and nine times out of ten, you wake up and it's solved. Don't ask me how. It just happens.'

The table allows a sheep to be 'walked' from the pen before you put its backside on the rollers. Once it's on the table, the sheep is naturally cast and totally relaxed. Prior to shearing, its legs are secured with the two bungee cords. A foot pedal works the rollers to turn the sheep around. There's a tray to collect wool and the table can be turned and swivelled. 'Everything's ergonomically correct,' says the inventor.

Des
Counting the benefits

'I hope you're not doing a send-up of lunatic inventors,' says Des Rainey, right at the outset. He's a tad suspicious of people who turn up with pens and cameras, looking for a story. Too often, he's seen the facts get swamped by the stereotypes. And he most certainly doesn't want that to happen with his mathematical learning aid, the Fun Abacus. 'I'm dead serious about this,' he says. 'It could really help our kids.'

But Des is the first to concede that its potential is not immediately obvious. 'It's the sort of thing, when you look at it, you think there couldn't be much in it.' Even those whose job it is to instruct the young can't initially see how it might help. 'I've shown it to teachers and they just look and say "What does it do?" But only a minute later, once I've pointed out one or two things, they're hooked on it.'

If the Fun Abacus looks like a novelty toy, it's probably because that's where the idea came from. Seeing 'one of those Click-Clacks, the things with the balls on them that you swing round to make a noise' was the trigger for Des and 'the idea grew from there'. He built the prototype himself, but then used a designer to improve his original version. One feature of the manufactured item he's now producing is that one Fun Abacus can be 'plugged into' others for exercises involving a larger number of numbers. The balls can also be removed, or swapped for others of a different colour, to assist understanding of various mathematical processes.

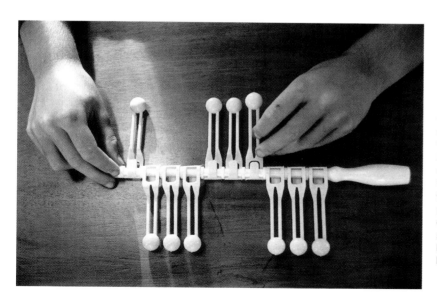

The Abacus in action. The toy's grown out of a long-standing interest Des has had in maths education and aims to make 'maths operations highly transparent and a good deal more fun'. For older children, the Abacus can introduce notions like fractions, decimals and percentages. It will even be applied to areas like statistics, geometry and binary numeration – the basis of computer function.

Where it began. Des modified a toyshop Click-Clack to produce the original Fun Abacus. It's only one of many inventions he's produced. Now approaching his 71st birthday, he says 'inventing keeps you going'. Having an eight-year-old helps as well.

Having an eight-year-old son at large within the estates has been of great assistance to Des. As he's developed his aid, young LLani has been a willing guinea pig, regularly testing new ideas and applications. Along the way, he's picked up an understanding of addition, subtraction, multiplication and division considerably in advance of his years. It's almost alarming to see him whiz through complex exercises that would beggar the befuddled brain of many an adult, were they denied access to a calculator.

But that is precisely the benefit the Abacus offers, says Des. As a qualified psychologist he's prepared a very detailed series of workbooks to be used in conjunction with his invention. 'The workbooks are important,' he says, because they're the map, the owner's manual. They outline games such as 'Whirl, Twirl and Strike', 'Swingo Bingo' and 'Fun Abacus Snap', all of which introduce essential concepts in a fun way. Exercises are especially tailored for pre-schoolers and older children, right through to the age of ten or eleven. With the help of the workbooks, the Abacus can even teach 'the first steps in algebra'.

No wonder he's serious about it. 'This is an exploration toy,' says Des. 'It lets children create, imagine and explore.' And they love doing it. 'They can pick up tables in less than a minute. If the books are taken in sequence, and the work's done properly, the results are great.'

At the most basic level children can use the Fun Abacus to solve problems such as how many fours there are in ten.

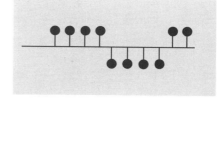

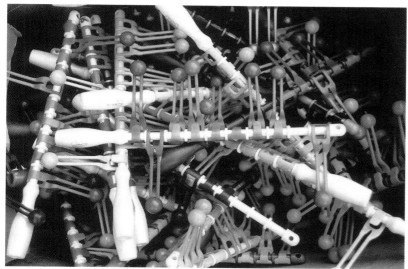

Des has just returned from a visit to the States, where his invention got an enthusiastic reception. He's contemplating launching it there under the brand name 'Pebblez', an allusion to the balls used in the aid.

Douglas

The anti-thumb thumper

Thumbs up! What else can you say? This is the invention every bruised digit's been waiting for. And it took a good bruising to get it invented. That happened the day Douglas Chell was working for a friend, putting on a roof. The iron was particularly thick and extra effort was needed to drive the nails home. So when he did, inevitably, hit his finger, it was a right royal, full-bodied blow. Even more painful than such contacts usually are. The wound needed stitching and further work on the roof looked unlikely. 'So I got a piece of PVC pipe and put a magnet inside it,' Douglas recalls. 'I put the nails against that and it worked magic.'

In the five years since then, that initial shield's changed quite considerably. The magnet's moved to the outside, fitted at the base of a little groove. The PVC pipe's gone, replaced by a more conformist shape, with two pieces of foam rubber on the inside. Initially, he thought the Safety Nailer would find favour with carpenters and the DIY brigade. That hasn't proved to be so, although he's had some positive feedback. 'One guy built a house with these. He was arthritic and couldn't bring his fingers back together. So he used the magnet, right through the job.'

Unexpectedly, his invention's been a hit, so to speak, in kindergartens. 'You hear some horrific stories,' says Douglas. 'The little kids haven't quite got the coordination. Teachers love it, because they don't have to hold the nail. When they're holding it, the kids try to whack it, big time.' The foam rubber inserts have allowed Douglas to recycle mouldings originally made for adults. 'They're real handy with this new market. I've used the foam rubber to fit four-year-old's fingers.'

With the Safety Nailer ticking over, Douglas is also developing a small business 'researching and improving windmills'. One of the things he's trying to do at the moment is modify an earlier invention to run on wind power. That invention is the Zephyr pump. Intended to pump water, it's an air pump 'with no moving parts inside'. He uses one himself, operated by a compressor. 'The compressor pushes air into the three chambers inside,' Douglas explains. 'The chambers act as a venturi and push water up the other side. It means, if you've got a well, you can pump water with air pressure.' So far, he's 'done half' of the new version that will connect to a windmill. But work's stopped. Douglas has 'run out of money, like a lot of inventors'.

Still, in the end, he says, 'It's not really about the monetary side. I've invented heaps of things and had a lot of fun with them. But I'm not a good salesman. If you've got a good salesman, you can do lots more. I'm happy finding something that someone needs. The satisfaction is looking at it and saying, I did that.'

Douglas Chell, inventor of the Safety Nailer. He says he's always been interested in inventions 'in the safety line, that are accessible to the people'.

The Nailer at work. The nail's held in place by a small circular magnet at the centre of the groove.

The Zephyr pump has no moving parts. Douglas operates this one with a compressor, but he's looking at wind options.

Ken

Giving energy a new spin

They don't crop up too often because, by and large, those who report the world regard the worst news as the best news. But, every so often, news reaches us of claims that someone's come up with 'another Kiwi world-beater'. We like these reports and want them to be true. There's something irresistibly heroic about the idea of the plucky little battler who does what all the world's money and megacorps can't manage. It confirms the 'guerilla' belief we have that we can outwit the wealthy any day, that all we need to stick it to the toffs is a healthy dose of ingenuity and self-reliance. We're convinced Pearce did it, and Rutherford and Gallagher, and the modern tales of Amon at Ferrari, Pickering at NASA, Blake on the boat and Britten on the track convince us we can still do it.

Ken Pedlar: I was born curious.

And this invention may provide the most compelling evidence of all. It is possible that Ken Pedlar has something that isn't just a 'world-beater'. It is possible he has invented a world-transformer. He's quite matter-of-fact about it. But quietly emphatic as well. 'We led the way in atomic energy,' he says, 'with Rutherford. And in DNA, with Francis Tripp. The basic discovery there was made by a New Zealander. Now we've got another one.'

That other one is his one. A solid object which, he says, does something no other solid object in the universe can do — or should be able to do. In the process, it has the potential to change the way we provide, store and transport energy. It will stand alongside the work of Rutherford and Tripp in the fields of atomic energy and DNA. 'These three great discoveries came out of here,' he says, 'good old New Zealand. And look at the effect they've had on the world.'

Even allowing for the fact that the effects of his invention have yet to be generally felt, it's a mind-boggling assertion. Unless you're Ken, in which case it's quite straightforward. 'It will succeed. That's already set in concrete. There's no way you can bowl it over. It's as simple as that.' 'Already, there's a factory, employing ten people. He's got patents approved or pending in 111 countries, and numerous agreements to build products under licence. There's one product already on the market, a small, water-driven electrical generator, called Nomad. It's a 'micro-power station producing a kilowatt or so', designed for remote-site and Third World applications. In developed countries it would probably be used

The Nomad is already being manufactured. It is the first product to emerge from the factory that harnesses the potential of the rotor. Here, Ken checks a moulding machine producing casings for the generator.

in conjunction with batteries for storage and an inverter to convert DC to 230 volts, so that 'you can run everything' off it. In poorer areas, it could operate as a stand-alone power source. 'It'll work anywhere you've got water,' says Kit Brooks, now working as Ken's project manager. 'If you've got no power, but you have got a creek, you just run water to the generator through a length of pipe. It's such a simple generator, there's only one moving part.'

That single moving part is Ken's crucial invention, the device he calls 'the rotor'.

In the Nomad generator, it's made of magnetic metals and relies on water pressure to spin. In fact, it 'rides' on a film of water passing through the centre of the plastic tube. But the rotor can also be made of non-magnetic materials like aluminium. The first impression is of a mushroom on a thick stem. It looks a bit like the world's best top. 'That's one definition of it,' says Kit, adding that a better one would be to call it the world's first shaftless flywheel. Which may not mean much to many, but if you understand the significance of that, you'll begin to understand the significance of the invention.

Flywheels are tantalising things. They've always had potential as stabilisers and for energy storage. The limitation's been that they couldn't move, largely because of inertia. You might dimly remember inertia from high school science. It's the thing that flung you over the handlebars when some pillock stuck a stick between the spokes of your bike. It's why you get a groin strain trying to move a 16-tonne weight. Inertia is the resistance of things to change or, put another way, their tendency to keep on doing whatever it is they've just been doing.

Inertia's the reason behind 'the one limiting factor of flywheel technology to date', according to Kit. That being the need for a flywheel to be fixed to an axle to restrain it. If, somehow, you could eliminate inertia, flywheels wouldn't need to be fixed in this way. You could have a flywheel that wasn't on an axle and wasn't fixed in place. Something that would continue to spin, and do the

Levitation achieved through the use of superconducting materials. It is the special properties of these materials that keep the spinning rotor, made of magnetic materials, floating in space. Sealed inside a casing, an arrangement like this would be at the heart of the planned rotor battery.

job you want it to do, without being secured by conventional means. And that's what Ken's got.

His rotor doesn't need an axle. Once started, it will keep spinning merrily away, all by itself. That happens because it does something no solid object should be able to do. Ken's rotor will spin in two planes simultaneously. When it's standing still, when it's stationary. In his factory, there's a small, 2 kg demonstration rotor. When it's fired up with compressed air it goes round and round, horizontally, like a top on a table. And it goes round and round vertically, like a wheel on the road. On the spot. At the same time. Coloured markings on the rotor show the two movements occuring, even though they shouldn't be.

It's either breaking the rules or escaping them. And whichever it is, the result is that it's not influenced by what's going on around it. So it can be kept in a moveable container. The container can be on its side, upside down, bouncing about, even rolling down a hill and it won't affect the performance of the rotor. Compare that with a normal flywheel on an axle. If the axle's part of a permanent structure, nothing can go anywhere. If the axle's tipped, so's the flywheel. And its function is totally or partially impaired.

There will be people reading this who'll be shaking their heads and muttering darkly that it can't be done. That there's some mischief afoot. Not so, says Ken. Just years of hard work. 'Science was always my forte,' he says. 'I loved science. I was born curious.' He recalls the last two pages of his high school general science text. 'It was an explanation of the problem of maintaining high-temperature plasma stability in breeder reactors.' Unlikely as it may seem to anyone who struggled to remember the chemical symbols, this fascinated Ken. He began studying plasma physics. In light of what was to happen, it was a propitious act.

About one thing, Ken's emphatic. 'The rotor was an absolute fluke. It only started because I happened to see a pure plasma ball. There's no way in the world that [the rotor] was coming here without me witnessing that.' When he

Seen from its base, this is the rotor itself. The design derives from Ken's chance sighting of a plasma ball in a substation. The upper surface of the rotor is a half-circle, not dissimilar in form to the curved section of the base of the 'stem'.

did, his studies were invaluable. 'I was working for the Auckland Electric Power Board, on the switching gear. And this day, the switch jammed as it was opening. But, instead of three arcs of energy arcing out, it formed into a ball. I was six feet away from it, looking directly at this damn thing. I watched it in mid-air and I could see the energy wave spinning vertically and horizontally. The waves were passing through each other. And that was the start.'

He set out to reproduce in solid form what he'd seen, with the plasma ball as his only clue. 'People say you need a match to light a fire. What I saw was the fire. But how to find the match that lights it, that was the job. The difficulty was trying to conceptualise an object that did not exist in the universe.' He decided that, since the ball was perfectly round, whatever he produced had to be similar. 'It had to be not quite a wheel and not quite a cylinder. So I did a lot of study, deep physics, trying to understand the phenomenon. Once I understood the energy form, I could slowly backtrack from there.' That was not an easy process. 'It was a long, long intellectual munch. From the time of the plasma ball to the time of physically making the rotor was a period of fourteen years.'

Ken made that first rotor at his workbench, 'out of a round sinker, a fishing sinker', testing it equally simply by just spinning it with his fingers. 'The thing was, by that time, I knew what I was looking for.' And once he'd found it, he refined it. 'The rotor is a very precise quantum object,' he says. 'If it's out by one percent, the damn thing's all over the show.' Ken decided early on that he wouldn't let New Zealand know much about it. 'There are a lot of problems here, especially with the great Kiwi knocking machine. And the principles of science are rarely understood in this country.' He's also 'very disillusioned with the education system. It's a good ten to fifteen years behind the rest of the world. The frontiers of physics are moving so fast now, it's not funny.' He cites the recent confirmation 'of the fifth force, anti-gravity. It's been confirmed by recent cosmological studies of planetary bodies and in high-energy physics labs.' What that means, he says, is 'that gravity's not the boss any more. A whole new civilisation's being developed out of that.'

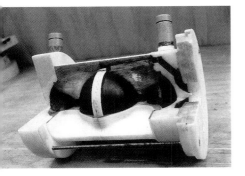

A cutaway of the interior of a Nomad generator. Water passing through the void spins the rotor, which produces the current. The rotor is the only moving part of the whole design, which will be made in a range of sizes.

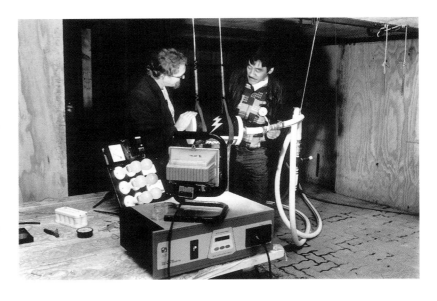

Advisor Craig Phipps-Black (left) and Ken (right) with a trial rig they have set up for tests on the Nomad generator. The generator itself hangs between them, suspended from two cables. When water's run through it, the Nomad will power pieces of equipment or illuminate the six lights on the panel on the table.

He's confident the rotor will be part of it. A key project is a battery combining ceramic materials known as superconductors and a rotor made of magnetic minerals. Those minerals are important, because superconductors have the capacity to repel magnets. So, if a magnetic rotor can be surrounded by superconductors, they'll combine to keep it hovering, levitating in space. Now, in the simplest of terms, if a casing's wrapped around those core ingredients and electricity, from mains, solar panels or a wind source, is used to spin the rotor, the result is what Kit calls 'a magnetic flywheel battery'.

'When you think about it,' he says, 'we've got no convenient way to store energy. If you wanted to take it, say, across the road, you could use a car battery or a can of petrol. But there's really no other way. If we had a flywheel, good, but it's no good if it's on a shaft. With this, we could have truly portable energy.' And Ken agrees. 'Mankind doesn't have efficient energy storage systems. Billions have been spent on flywheels, but there's always been the problem of centrifugal force and frictional losses. This eliminates that.'

But he has other plans as well. As someone who 'grew up in the flight path at Auckland airport' and later worked there, he's always had an interest in aviation. His particular passion is disc aircraft. 'They are the most efficient you can get for vertical take-off and landing.' A long-distance version of such a craft would be a boon to New Zealand. 'It would solve the tyranny of distance. It's one asset I can leave my children, to see them through the centuries.' But, if it's to work, a disc aircraft requires stabilising, which flywheels can also be used for. It's another possible application for his rotor. 'I've spent thirty years testing and studying, to work out the dynamics,' says Ken. And he has a design which he believes will work. 'All the mathematics and science have been checked, checked and double-checked. Building it will be a walk in the park.'

That stroll may not happen for a while. The Nomad generators are a top priority. As is the Flywheel Battery. Ken says it's taken 36 months to get up and running but everything's now in place. 'The whole thing's structured, worldwide. 'It's already done. Past tense.' And, despite his concerns about 'the tall poppy syndrome' he's determined the technology must remain in New Zealand hands. 'It's all been set up so that the income and the technology stays here. There's far too much money for this country to lose.' It may sound incredible, but then, so does the notion of a solid object spinning two ways at once. Those who are sceptical, and those who are not, should all do the same thing. Watch this space.

Janet

Angling for safety

Never assume an invention has to be something radically new. By definition, great leaps forward are few and far between. Most inventions will only enhance what already exists. The Converta Desk is a perfect example. Sceptics be advised, this is an invention. And it's got an award to prove it. In 1997, Janet Dougherty won a gong for a concept she'd had 'for a long time'. But even though she's been recognised by her peers, the great-great-great-niece of the first Registered Nurse in the world still can't accept her desk makes her an inventor.

'I do feel like a real fraud,' she says. 'When I look at some of the other inventions I've seen, the things other people have come up with, I wonder how this compares.'

The point is, it doesn't have to. Her desk is an improvement, something that works better than other similar items. And that's all an effective invention has to do.

The essential features here are the keyboard tray and something Janet's called the Converta platform. The keyboard tray pulls out, as most do. But, drawing on her own nursing background and understanding of ergonomics, Janet paid a lot of attention to the dimensions. Measuring 800 x 400 mm, the tray's 'bigger than normal', she says, 'so it will comfortably hold a keyboard, mouse and calculator . . . the things you need when you're working'. The Converta platform is actually part of the desktop. But it's a separate part, which can be angled upwards. A groove at the base holds a ruler to support text or drawing paper. Ingeniously, there's also a groove for a ruler at the top to act as a temporary ledge for pens, rubbers, staplers and the like. In addition, the desk's

Another of Janet's creations, the KEYRite adjustable document holder is intended to enable users to sit straight on at the computer, as recommended in the New Zealand VDU Code of Practice. The KEYRite can tilt up to 60° (like the Converta platform on the desk) and be pulled over a standard keyboard.

supplied with a movable 10 mm metal bar that holds, and guides, a magnetic ruler.

Elementary as it may seem, that ruler proved to be a right royal hassle. 'It was going to cost thousands of dollars to get a ruler mould made up that would include the magnet,' recalls Janet. 'So we decided to glue the magnetic block on. It took months to get the glue right.' The other half of the 'we' Janet refers to is her business partner, Mike. Although she says she's always been handy — 'When I was a kid I spent hours playing with Dad's timber and blocks of wood' — she is, unfortunately, currently shedless. So it is exceedingly difficult for her to build what she designs.

Enter Mike, a furniture maker and, therefore, a shed owner. True, he lives a considerable distance away, but Janet says the collaboration's gone well. 'I do the drawings and send them to him, and he gets stuck in, hacking away and modifying. We both think outside the square, we have a good understanding. It works well.' And needless to say, she hopes people will find that her desk does too. 'The goal was to make the workplace a safe place. All I want now is for it to get out in the marketplace and prove itself.'

The Converta Desk's tilting platform allows users to write, draw, read or type. 'The whole concept was to be able to pull out and angle up at the same time,' says Janet. The desk's available in four lengths, the shortest being 1200 mm, the longest, 2 metres. Prices range from $550 to $630.

Keith

You can go over the top

Parental warning – the contents of this page may be harmful to your wealth. You might wish to conceal them from the fruit of your loins for fear the briefest glimpse of Keith Kerr's 'ferris wheel' swing triggers persistent demands that you get one too. The available evidence suggests it could happen. 'The only problem I've had so far,' says Keith, ominously, 'is arguments about who's getting on next. One day it was here there were half a dozen kids queuing up to have a go.'

This should come as no surprise. Ask any truly dedicated swinger. They'll confirm that their ultimate fantasy is a swing that goes all the way round, right over the top, in a great, swooping, stomach-tingling arc. On this swing you can do that. You can loop the loop. And stay the right way up the whole time. Little wonder it excites the young. Little wonder Keith thinks he's got a winner.

Two very different motivations inspired him to develop his swing. The first was a conversation about toys with his father-in-law. 'He happened to mention that he'd seen a toy that was like a seesaw, but wasn't a seesaw. I tried

Keith's swing is designed to carry one or two. 'It'll do several things. With two on, it's a seesaw, ferris wheel and swing combined. Then, for solo use, it's a swing.'

to get him to describe it,' says Keith, 'but he couldn't. I got a picture in my mind's eye of what he was trying to describe . . . I left it in my head for nine years.' It may well have stayed there, except that Keith lost his job, and couldn't find another one. Not full-time, anyway. For the best part of five years, he was unemployed. 'I'd do a bit of part-time work, then get laid off. One day, the rain was bucketing down, and I was pacing the floor, feeling frustrated. I thought, "What the hell am I doing walking round the house? I should be doing something." So I went straight down to the local engineers' and got the steel. I decided I was going to try that idea, it was either going to work or it wasn't.'

He borrowed a set of benders to shape the hoop. His brother-in-law, an engineer, helped 'get the bugs out'. Soon, the man who says he's 'not a long-term inventor' had finished building the first and, so far, the only example of his swing. His father-in-law came over. Thinking back to their discussion about toys, Keith asked him, 'Is this it? And he said, "Mate, I don't know, it's fifteen years since I've seen it." '

Since then, others have seen it. And been impressed. Keith's going through the costly business of patenting his swing. 'The biggest buzz I've had so far,' he says, 'is putting an idea into practice and actually seeing it work the way I intended it to.' The job now is to turn something that works into something that sells. With limited funds, that won't be easy. But, this is something that began with him trying to create his own employment through sheer desperation. And he's not planning to quit.

With patent applications close to completion, Keith's investigating manufacturing options. A firm in Australia's interested in building the swing for that market. Keith says it's too early to put a retail price on the design.

Paul

Stopping the rot

Forced to give up his job as a result of a back injury, Paul is now relying on his inventive skills to keep things going.

The junk mail flashes photos of them. Now, there are even ads on the telly. Suddenly, it seems, every man and his dog wants to sell us a dehumidifier. They're really an acknowledgement that our homes are still built, by and large, in the pioneer manner. We've finally got round to insulating the wall cavity, but our frugal tendency to bung in a single sheet of glass can still be a pane. Condensation is a problem in many Kiwi houses. But the solution can be simpler than a brand new dehumidifier. That's certainly what Paul's pinning his hopes on. And what inspired him to invent the Drysil.

A serious back injury had put him in hospital. When he came home he found sleep hard to come by. Prowling the house, he heard the trickle of water down windows. 'I could hear the drip, drip, drip of condensation. I could see how the chipboard was swelling and mottling.' Frustrated by the limitations of his injury, he felt this was something he could fix. So he took to the shed to solve the problem. Drysil was his answer. 'I did it for our own home first,' says

Paul, 'then friends got excited, asked me where I got it from. So I installed it for them too.'

He's put a lot of thought into something that looks pretty straightforward. Screwed and sealed to the sill, the right-angled channel is high enough to be effective and wide enough to 'get a cloth in', Paul says, adding that 'there's also room for the end of a vacuum cleaner nozzle. So it's easy to clean.' Getting the goo out of the corners is no hassle either, since the ends are fitted with 45° rubber bungs. Not only do they cover the fitting screws, they assist the wiper remove what's wiped. A small hole (or holes) drilled through the base of the window frame drains condensation to the outside of the house, thereby, as a BRANZ appraisal puts it, 'reducing the likelihood of fungal growth on and damage to linings, sills, other building elements and furnishings'.

Originally his invention was intended to be fitted to aluminium windows that don't include a condensation channel, but Paul's quick to point out it can just as easily be installed where a window does have a built-in channel, should that be too shallow or for some other reason is not doing the job. Now he's designed a version for wooden sills as well. This is a three-sided aluminium channel that can be rebated into the sill, with a waterproof tube to allow exterior drainage.

Drysil is 'the first thing I've invented', says Paul, 'but I've got another one on the go now. It's just a matter of raising the money to keep going.' In the meantime, he's got a BRANZ appraisal of his condensation diverter to overcome the fact that, as he puts it, 'I had no recognition in the building trade' and 'wanted some credibility'. That's starting to come, although he says it's been slow. 'But a hospital in Auckland's installing it now, then assessing if they should do more.' He's building up a network of installers who can 'do a three-bedroom house for six to eight hundred dollars. That's the cost to have it installed.'

A display model showing the condensation trap fitted to a window.

The traps feature triangle corner wedges for easy cleaning and drainage holes taking moisture to the outside.

Don in his shed with some early production units in the background. A friend with his own shed and lathe turned the wooden moulds for the plastic components on the table.

A detail of a typical pipe modification for outflow to the tanks.

Don

From sink to cistern — improved water works

Years of tinkering, of teaching, of making all manner of things and showing other people how to do the same, have culminated here in an invention that hosts of homeowners will be clamouring to have. Don's tackled a problem that's going to get bigger, and if councils throughout New Zealand don't endorse, refine and promote his solution, they want their heads read. Unhappily, the early indications that they might show some sense in this matter are not promising. 'The local councils know about it,' says Don somewhat testily, 'but they've just ignored it. They don't reply to my letters. They just treat me like I'm some local ning-nong.'

Well, he isn't. It should be clear to most people by now that we waste water. In fact, we do more than that. We squander the stuff. And that's what Don is out to stop. Although he doesn't live in Auckland, his invention was triggered when the big water shortage happened. 'I was having a shower, then I went to the loo. And I thought, why shouldn't the water in the shower flush the toilet. I thought someone must have done all this before. So I checked and found nothing and I decided to go for it.' And now, he says, he's reached the point of no return. 'I've invested so much money, I've got to keep going. So far, it's cost me $50,000 in development money.'

Normally, pouring that amount of money down the drain would be the cause of great concern. Unless, of course, one happens to be a redundant TV newsreader or former member of the Tourism Board. Since he is neither, it has caused Don some apprehension. Although he also accepts it was cash that had to be spent if he was going to conclusively prove the viability of an idea which seems, on the face of it, straightforward enough. But the mechanics of using water from a shower or bath, and other appliances such as dishwashers and washing machines, are complex and problematic. Only now, when he's into his fourth year of doing things, can Don say, 'We're just about there.'

One or two further official seals of approval are really all he needs. The testing's been done. The equipment he's designed, built and tested himself has proved how to harness the potential of waste, or 'grey', water. And that potential's considerable.

'Dishwashers use heaps of water,' Don points out. 'And the old washing machines, with an agitator, would use about ninety litres for four or five washes. The new machines, they say, they need less per fill, but you need several fills to complete a cycle. I tried it out, with a bucket. They use sixty litres of water on one rinse cycle.' All of which disappears into the sewage or stormwater system, requiring larger treatment plants and all the other associated paraphernalia. It'll still end up there, of course, even if a home has Don's ECO Waste Water Recycling System installed. But only after it's passed through the toilet cistern and become

A genuinely indigenous inventor, Don Sorensen recently discovered he had Ngai Tahu ancestry. He hopes New Zealand local government groups will investigate his system. 'It's not just about making money,' he says, 'it's about doing something for society, for the environment.'

what's known as 'black' water. This double use, turning grey water into black, means a significant reduction in the overall volume of waste liquid generated by a household. With a limited number of ECO systems already installed, 'users report seventy percent savings', he says.

Getting to this stage has had its trials and tribulations. His first experiments were pretty rudimentary. 'My proof-of-concept model was two rubbish bins, some lampshades I bought at The Warehouse, and whatever I could get from the kitchen — colanders, salad bowls, bits and pieces,' Don recalls. In a somewhat later version, 'I had the toilet system screwed to the outside of the house. And I had great difficulty getting the water into the toilet. I burnt out transformers and pumps galore.' There was another problem associated with showers, baths and washing machines. 'I had to get rid of the soap, or I was going to end up with a great big foaming Kiwi bidet,' says Don. He overcame that by using a principle known as flotation extraction.

Traditionally, flotation extraction's been a part of the lead mining process. What Don did here was adapt the mining technique, modifying the inside of the diversion pipe that's connected to the shower, bath and so on. At the point where the pipe runs into his storage tanks he installed a little weir. 'The weir foams up the water. And, of course, what foam there is rises, so it bypasses the tanks and goes straight to the gully trap. Any hair or lint or particles go there, too.' With foam, lint, hair and the like flotationally extracted, the household's grey water is stored in tanks until the cistern needs refilling. The ECO system uses a 12-volt pump operated by a microswitch attached to the toilet float valve. 'When the float goes down, the switch comes on to drive the pump,' Don explains. 'And when the float goes back up, the switch turns off.'

As for the storage tanks, in reticulated areas, they're normally installed outside, in the ground, near the house and by a gully trap. Properties with

Don's ECO system comes in four models — in-line and square configurations designed for houses with either one or two toilets.

No	Component
1	Shower
2	Bath
3	Washing machine
4	Toilet cistern
5	Washing machine waste water
6	Bath waste water
7	Shower waste water
8	Vent pipe
9	Gully trap
10	Recycled water pipe
11	Recycling system
12	12 volt/230 volt transformer
13	12 volt wire to pump
14	Wire to microswitch
15	Filter tank
16	Pump tank

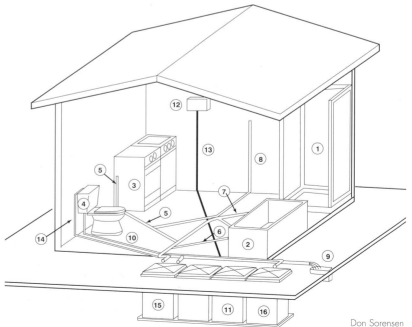

Don Sorensen

septic tanks can also use the system. Indeed, Don's found 'it helps to fix septic tank problems by reducing the volume through the tank'. Those who have them will know that when a septic tank floods, it can overload the leach field. This, in turn, leads to a build-up of bacteria and a most unsavoury pong. Faced with this very problem, and the threat of legal action from neighbours, Don says a local family installed an ECO system in desperation. 'When they put it in, the ground water level was 330 mm. Two months later, it was down to one metre.' And that, in every respect, went quite a long way towards clearing the air. Such benefits were not what Don had in mind at the outset. 'I did it to promote water saving. I never thought of septic tanks.'

Nor did he think he'd be up to his neck in rules and regulations either. Although that is how it's proved to be. His system 'has to comply with the Foul

Set into the ground, the storage tanks can be stored in a number of configurations. Generally they'd be in a line or form a square. They require little in the way of maintenance or cleaning. Chlorine tablets are dropped into dispensers at the top of the tanks once a week to prevent bacterial build-up and odours. Chlorine levels can be adjusted if a property has a septic tank.

Water laws, the Plumbing laws, this law, that law, every other bloody law. If you're going to use the water in your tanks for garden watering, you have to put a little sign up — a tap with a slash through it — so people know not to drink it. I decided to go for a BRANZ appraisal, to give it some outside credibility. Normally, that takes three months. Up to now it's taken a year and four months. I've got so many documents I'm damn near up to ISO 9000. The inspectors are too scared to say "Yes" unless they've gone through all the channels. It's the compliance costs that are stopping people doing things. It's become so bloody expensive because they've gone overboard. A lot of times, I think this is what stops people. To be fair, I can see what they're about. This is something brand new, it's never been done in New Zealand. Maybe I'm just that flaming pig-headed I won't let things stop me.'

Being pig-headed may have helped. But so has his background as a mechanic and technical teacher. Both jobs have given him plenty of practice in solving things. 'A lot of the things you make are small inventions. They're ways to solve problems. Where I teach, a lot of the students have ten-speeds. They've got very thin wheels, which tend to get bent in a normal bike stand. So I came up with an idea where the handlebars hung off the stand. And I've designed a four-wheeled tipping trailer that's tipped by the car backing. It still sits there, in the background, waiting to be developed.'

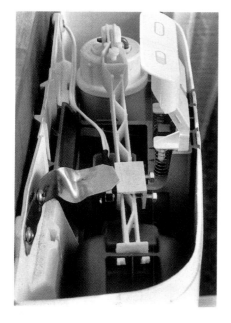

A microswitch installed in the cistern controls the pump that supplies grey water from the tanks.

Obviously, for the moment, the ECO system is taking priority. A friend who is retired has lent a hand along the way. A fellow sheddie, with an ancient lathe, he turned out a range of wooden moulds as patterns for the aluminium masters needed to produce various mouldings. Other than that, Don says, 'I'm it. Everything from the managing director to the bum boy. I do the lot.' One thing he won't do is repeat a mistake made by his grandfather, many years ago. 'He actually invented the first ever stumping jack — to pull stumps out of the ground. Well, it went to his head. He hired a hansom cab, started going up and down the main street. Then, some bugger came along and pinched the idea and patented it. The family got nothing. Well, that and another similar tale made me think, I've come across a lot of "If only" people. I just think, if you've got something, then go for it. We've only got one life to lead. And it's not just inventions, it's lots of things — feelings, plans. You can't end up saying "If only" about it.'

Tony

Watching the waste

Plumbers are notoriously hard to get. Possibly because it's their job to fix things that are notoriously hard to get at. Take the 25 mm nuts under a hot water cylinder. If you're waiting for a plumber who happens to be battling with them, you might very well become impatient. Probably because the plumber is, as well. It's something Tony Allnut knows all about. As a plumber, he's had to wrestle with the nut problem. And it's very awkward. 'You've got to lie on your back. The tools never grip properly. With the other pipes so close, there's no swing distance.' At least, there wasn't until he invented a right-angle spanner. Somebody else may have had a similar idea, he says, but if so, he's never seen it.

Nor has he ever seen anything like his tap reseater. It's a simple tool that does a fiddly job. Reseating's 'like a valve grind', says Tony. It's necessary because taps get gunk in them and they drip, so we tighten them. That wears the thread out, so the tap drips more, so we tighten it again, and so it goes. Until the plumber arrives. Attached to a drill, Tony's tap reseater will 'ream a tap out in place. One spin and it's fine.' He's also designed a spring-action device that can be fitted to a standard tap to conserve water.

But if nuts and taps are troublesome things, drains are even worse. Frustrated by the time wasted trying to work out where a blockage occurred, Tony knew the solution was something he couldn't afford. 'I needed a reasonably priced camera' for drain inspections. And since there weren't any, he decided to build one himself. It's one hundred percent domestic, all the parts have been bought off the shelf in New Zealand'. A control panel allows the operator to

The tap reamer can refurbish a dripping tap quickly and without the need to remove it. Tony sees it as being particularly valuable in areas with harder water.

watch live colour images from the camera and also check just how far down the pipe it is.

Like many other inventive persons, Tony's encountered a huge number of problems and unforseen events. 'It's been a good lesson in perseverance.' One hassle was actually getting the camera down a drain. Then it proved hard to get it round corners. Both difficulties were overcome with 'small wheels on the camera, six at each end. They keep the camera in the centre of the pipe.' A flexible fibreglass rod pushes it along. And, when Tony found the video cable could be damaged if used to pull the camera out, he fitted a universal joint, 'as on the drive shaft of a car', so that the pushing rod could safely pull 'without strain on the cable'.

With all the bugs ironed out, and the camera on the job, prying into the murkiest depths like some robo-paparazzi, Tony quietly declares himself 'quite pleased with it now, at the end of its evolution'. Others are too, it would seem. There's been 'a lot of interest from Master Plumbers all around the country'. Not surprising really, when Tony estimates the final price will be about $8,000 while alternatives cost around $30,000. Despite the huge difference, Tony insists his self-built, trial-and-error invention offers 'picture quality that's exactly the same. There's nothing better on the market.'

The kind of image the camera produces, deep inside a pipe. Tony had to design a separate housing for the lights, to ensure heat didn't damage the camera itself. It was a problem he solved despite, he says, having no skills as an electrician.

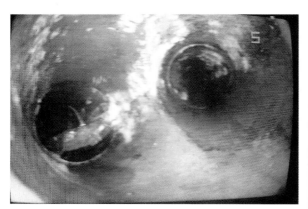

Tony's video camera is designed for one-person use. It's intended for 100 mm household drains, although larger wheel arrays would allow it to be used to inspect local body networks, which tend to use 150 mm pipes.

Tony has invented a number of plumbing-related items in his shed, including the Wet Shower Tray, which is designed to sit on the floorboards so householders can avoid the sort of radical surgery necessary for installation of a conventional shower, namely cutting large holes in the floor.

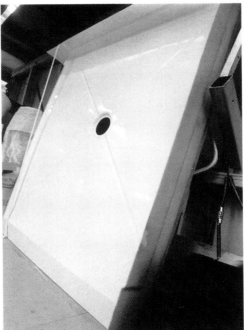

The Wet Shower Tray's specifically aimed at people whose mobility's been seriously impaired, since it's then that bathrooms often need to be remodelled. At 1200 x 1200, the tray's large enough to accommodate a wheelchair. It costs between $300 and $1,000.

Sid

There's no stopping him

Round Sid Hurst's way, people have 'lost most things other than their mortgages'. The church was one of the few services left 'and that's about to close . . . they seem to stick it into the country all right'. When you're facing that kind of adversity, you have to be resourceful. It's as well, then, that there are, Sid says, inventive genes in a lot of farmers. 'Some of mine invent ways of getting out of trouble.' Indeed, there's a family tradition of doing similar things. In the early years of the 20th century, Sid's uncle actually 'invented the Band Aid, and made a million out of it.'

To date, no such largesse has come his way. But some of his uncle's influence has obviously rubbed off, even if his inventions aren't as therapeutic. One early idea, for electric fences, was a 'a bang-on ceramic insulator'. He thinks it was the first of its kind and, perhaps because of that, it didn't take off. He has higher hopes for his latest idea, about which he will say very little. Only that it's a doozie, that plenty of people will want one and that it's to do with fencing.

So is his most visible invention, the Electromatic gate. Not your common or garden gate, this. Not the kind you have to hop out of your vehicle to open, then drive through, hop out again, go back to close, and then drive off. With this gate you just point your farmbike or ute straight at it and keep on going. Sid built and tested the first one himself, although later he farmed production out. That original gate was something of a collaborative effort. The hinges that let it open and close unassisted were invented by a friend of his, Ross Mitchell. Ross had designed them for a gate of his own, but they were also ideal for Sid's concept.

Invention is in the blood for Sid.

A detail of the spring-loaded system Sid is using on his gate.

Finding something effective to act as a buffer has been more problematic. 'I've always had trouble,' says Sid, 'finding a tip that didn't mark cars or come off. It was the same with the guy who started making ladies hairpins. They kept falling out till he put bends in them.' Over the years, Sid's tried fibreglass rods and rubber tips. He'd have probably given hairpins a go if he'd thought they'd work. But now, on what he call his 'Mark 10 version', he's got the answer. It's a set of small, belting wheels that stay on the gate and leave the paint on the vehicle.

As for the gates? 'I couldn't farm without them,' says Sid. 'I don't know how we'd manage. They're ideal for people who're going through gates a lot. They're not suited to tractors. And they're not suited to farmers who're not careful.' These limitations may explain why sales have slowed in recent years. Although Sid sees another factor at work. 'If you try to sell things to farmers, they think they can make it themselves. So it has to be cheap. But because the drive-through costs twice as much as an ordinary gate, they say "I'll get out and keep opening the gate".'

The gate is ideal for smaller vehicles like this ATV. Sid says tractors can smash them, unless they're driven slowly. The gates can be electrified to make sure that stock don't go through them as easily as a vehicle can. A simple spring clip and lead, attached to an electric fence, runs a current through the gate.

But he's pressing on. While not actively promoting the Electromatic gate, as he once did, he's 'still got a guy who'll make them if people want them'. He also sees a potential new market as more and more people move to lifestyle blocks and begin to dabble with hobby farming. He's hoping the Range Rover cockies might share his dislike of dismounting and opt for the cruise-through alternative. If it happens, he's not sure it'll come in time to reverse the decline in the area he's farmed in since he was 64. Now 80, Sid's content that the gates have proved their point, and their value. And there's still that other, top secret idea to work on. Something else that will make a small but significant difference. 'When you think of what I've seen in my lifetime,' he says, 'what's someone who's twenty now going to see in their's?'

These small wheels on the latest version of the drive-through gate act as a buffer, preventing damage to the paintwork or body panels of a vehicle.

Ross Mitchell's modified hinge is a key feature of Sid's gate. It allows it to close of its own accord.

Colin
Geared up for racing

'The garage is mine,' says Colin. 'I do what I like in here.' Raised on a farm, Colin thought 'bugger the sheep and went engineering instead'. A lot of the equipment he's got here has been added since he started work on his invention. Originally, he used the bonnet of 'a derelict old XJ 6' as a workbench.

Last Christmas, Colin Kingsbury took the plunge. With considerable apprehension, to be sure, because it was a big step. But, faced with the need to make certain precision parts, he went out and bought a King Rich Tool Room Milling Machine. No hobby machine this, it's a very flash piece of kit. And so it should be, with a price tag in excess of $10,000. Or more, in view of the aftermath. Colin's wife felt his priorities were not all they might have been. She rather saw the purchase as a case of King Rich, Queen Poor. And politely suggested a need for balance. 'So I compromised,' says Colin, with a grin, 'and we got a new kitchen as well.'

Now all parties are poorer but happier, and work on the invention continues apace. It's an idea that's come from the race track and is likely to end up back there as well. He's got an novel and inexpensive solution to a problem that's bothered a number of his 'friends in the race game'. It surfaced one weekend when a mate came back from a meeting complaining about his gears. 'He kept

missing a gear. When he was meant to be in second, he kept going into top.' Knowing that Colin was a bit of a shed wizard, he asked if something could be done.

It was a challenge Colin couldn't resist. He knew that Formula One cars used sequential gear boxes, in which the gear lever travels in a straight line when gears are changed, rather than going through a 'gate' as normal manual systems do. But he also knew that the purpose-built gearboxes fitted to the Ferraris and McLarens and Minardis of the Grand Prix circuit cost a lot more than the King Rich and the kitchen combined. 'A true sequential system's very simple,' he says. 'It has a hydraulic ram and, as it moves, it pushes and pulls the selectors. But they're very expensive, big bucks. They can be up to $50,000.'

That's a lot more than any of his friends could invest. Something 'affordable for the average guy' was needed. He set out to find it. 'The first few

Don't panic if somebody says 'Give us a KASS'. They'll be talking about this, the Kingsbury Automotive Sequential System. There's one final problem Colin's working to solve. 'It'll occasionally go to neutral before finding the next gear. I know how to fix it,' he says, but it's proving to be a bit tricky. He expects to overcome that in a month or so and is already working on a Mark 2 version. In response to requests, it will feature 'an electronic read-out on the dash, so you can tell what gear you're in'.

ideas I had didn't work.' He was at the point of abandoning the whole thing, until he got talking to a rally driver in the pub one night. 'He couldn't change down quick enough. And he said it would be good to have a sequential that would preselect. So you could go from top to second and jump third.' Just yarning about the idea, Colin began to see how it could be done. 'And that put me into a whole different train of thought. I thought, "Hey, I know how to do this." That was it. I was up in the middle of the night, working on the computer.'

And after that, in the shed making the blueprints real. But that reality wasn't a sequential gearbox. It was something far cheaper and simpler. Colin's reality was an attachment that would allow an ordinary gearbox to behave as if it was a sequential gearbox. 'It's the only way I can make it work,' he says. And he has. After 'about three or four years' enhancing, refining, testing and retesting his invention, 'it's about ninety-nine percent there'.

Already patented, he's produced 'a bolt-on attachment and modified linkages', designed to fit to any standard racing gearbox. 'There's no physical harm to the box. It just involves taking off one shaft and putting another on.' Colin's understandably guarded about the inner workings of the Kingsbury Automotive Sequential System, as he's named it. But he estimates it'll cost around $1,500 for a unit to bolt on to the gearbox. 'It's not quite as good as the real McCoy,' he says. 'Then again, if you've got the dollars for the real McCoy, go for it.' In fact, he may be too modest. As a result of that conversation with the rally driver, his system can preselect gears, something 'true sequentials can't do, because of the way they're programmed'.

Current plans are to have a perfected system 'up and running for the next race season'. He'd like to see some out on the track, racing. 'That's what we need, just to ease the way in.' If reaction's positive in what he concedes is 'a niche market' he'll make the attachments himself, 'keeping production reasonably small'. For the moment, he's just pleased he has confounded the sceptics, 'all those people who come up to me and say you can't do that'. Well, says Colin, 'I don't like that word "can't". And now I can show them, "Yes, I can." The thing does work. I'd like to recoup the money I've spent, sure. But I've done what I set out to do. It works. And that's the biggest buzz.'

Nick

An anchor up on top

When you've fallen off a roof not once, not twice, but three times, and each time avoided serious injury, you know you've been lucky. When a close relative, working at a disability centre, tells you 'every month, they see someone who has had a fall and ended up a quadriplegic' you realise luck's not enough. When the price of a fall can be a life, or last a lifetime, you need something more certain. And since it's never going to be possible to completely prevent accidents, you should try to prevent the consequences. That's what Nick Collins has done with his invention, the Anchor Bracket. In effect, it's an ambulance halfway down the cliff, a way to eliminate the risks of the unavoidable. 'If you're working on a roof, the moment you bend over, you're off balance. You fall forward, so your head or neck is the first thing to hit the ground.' Except, with his anchor, you don't go that far.

Nick originally got the idea in his days as a roofer, working on a large commercial site. He and his crew had all the necessary safety gear, some bought especially for the contract. Nick chanced to ask, 'Once the roof's on, what do we hook on to? And the guy just shrugged. We were fourteen metres up on that job.' The basic idea has undergone a good deal of development since then. He says he's 'onto the Mark 3 model now'. But the objective's never changed. From the outset, he wanted to improve the odds, especially for those in the industry. 'The average person involved in construction is between 25 and 35. Most of them have got young families. If kids lose their father, that's for ever.'

Today, he says, a number of roof claddings are sold with warranties requiring cleaning at scheduled intervals or similar specified maintenance. That means more people doing more work on the roof which, in turn, increases the need for an invention like his. Tougher OSH requirements are also upping the safety ante. 'Even now,' Nick says, 'anybody facing the possibility of falling further than three metres has to have barrier protection or a fall arrest system.'

Tests on the zinc-plated Bracket indicate it will withstand loads up to 1500 kg.

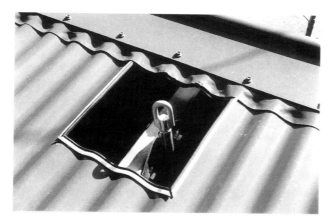

Not only will the invention withstand considerable loads, it's also designed to work when installed upside down, should a roof design require that.

One of the key features of his Anchor Bracket is that it works as a fall arrest system before the cladding's in place, as it's being installed and later, when maintenance or painting is required.

Used in conjunction with a safety harness, the Bracket has several components. There's a main anchor plate, that's fitted to one side of a truss, with a backing plate on the other. The anchor plate has a threaded shaft into which an eye-bolt is screwed, once a 16 mm hole has been drilled in the cladding. Anyone working on a roof would clip their safety harness to the bolt. It's removed when not in use and the thread sealed with a nylon plug, Tek screw

The three holes on the anchor plate and backing plate allow for angle adjustment when fitting to match a range of roof profiles. Nick also envisages that manufacturers could 'put the brackets on before they send their trusses to the site'.

Nick installed the first Anchor Bracket he ever made on a truss in his garage.

and Profile washer. Nick says, 'Each roof would be taken on its merits,' when deciding where to locate Anchor Brackets, but generally, 'on a standard single-gable roof, there'd be one or more on each side, near the gutter line'. When someone attaches their safety harness to the eye-bolt, they should ensure they have a safe working radius, or half-circle, in which they can work. In the worst case, that safe radius should ensure a fall is checked before the worker goes over the edge of the roof.

While the brackets could be retro-fitted to an existing roof by 'removing a sheet of iron or cutting a square out and putting a patch over', he sees the most likely initial application in new houses. 'The cost to put them in a house from new would be about three to four hundred dollars. But they're there permanently.' At present, he's 'trying to get it into the MasterSpec' and has had positive reaction elsewhere. 'A lot of architects think it's brilliant. The job is to educate people to use it. If we can save one life through it, at least I've done something. All you need is five minutes' preparation and you've got that security.'

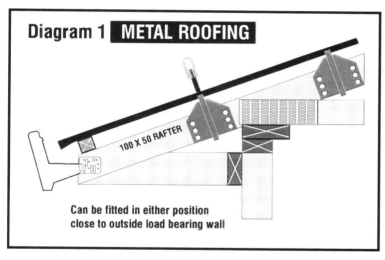

Diagram 1 METAL ROOFING

100 X 50 RAFTER

Can be fitted in either position close to outside load bearing wall

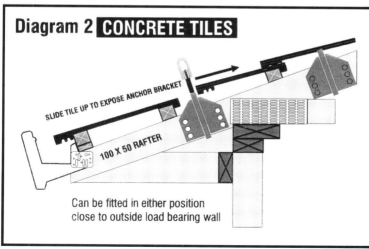

Diagram 2 CONCRETE TILES

SLIDE TILE UP TO EXPOSE ANCHOR BRACKET

100 X 50 RAFTER

Can be fitted in either position close to outside load bearing wall

The Anchor Bracket can be fitted to either traditional metal roofing or to concrete tile roofs.

Nick Collins

Looking not unlike a rocket motor, the tubes are actually where the 'paper petrol' goes.

The classic DIY inventor, Sam's on a mission to find a use for the useless.

Sam
More heat from the press

Eighty years ago, there was nothing nostalgic about traction engines. At the beginning of the 20th century, those lumbering, thundersome monsters were still the cutting edge of technology. Or at least, that's the way Sam Miller remembers them. As 'a kid growing up on the farm' he loved to watch the great engines out thrashing in the paddock. And years later, just before his eightieth birthday, that memory sparked an unusual plan. 'I decided,' says Sam, 'when I retire, I'll make a steam car.' And he did.

It's quite possible that there is no car like Sam's car anywhere else in the world. Steam cars certainly aren't new. Some, like the Stanley Steamer, have even been commercially successful. But what makes this one unique is the fuel stock.

Newspapers have a proven capacity to get a country cross, but Sam's the first to use them to get across country. Confronted with the shocks and horrors of a dysfunctional world, Sam's turned revulsion into propulsion, using crises and conflicts, murder and mayhem — not to mention crosswords, recipes and personal ads – to get about.

Having rolled yesterday's headlines into 'paper logs', they go into a boiler at the rear of the old Austin A40. 'You use a small log to light them,' he explains, 'like kindling. The cylinders take a dozen logs which fire the boiler and allows the A40 to run at a top speed of thirty ks. Not fast, but it goes.' Sam says someone asked him once how long the car actually goes for. 'I said it depends how hot the news is.' In fact, twelve paper logs will keep the car going for two hours. Wreathed in steam and hissing pipes, he's driven the car about twenty times. 'Just test drives round the race course or paddocks — never on the open road.'

Newspapers are at the heart of another of Sam's inventions, the free-standing heater. Its merit's been externally recognised with a second-equal placing in the Best Idea category of the 1996 ECNZ Rutherford Awards. Confronted

Left: An interior shot showing the three holes into which the paper logs are fitted.

Right: The kindling to spark the conflagration is inserted through these smaller holes.

with a pile of papers requiring disposal, it occurred to Sam that it was a waste of energy. He thought, 'There's a lot of heat in newspaper. I'll see if I can't work it so it could be used.'

The heater runs on three 'paper logs', each comprising about five issues of the local daily. 'It has to be free-standing,' Sam explains, 'to get the paper in the back. Three rolls last a couple of hours and it gives a really good heat. There's only a wee bit of ash and it disappears next time. I empty it once a month.'

So far, this eminently sensible idea hasn't reached the market, even though it would seem ideally suited to baches, workshops and sheds. Anywhere, in fact, where use is intermittent or the neighbours don't want their papers. Sam admits there might be some resistance to the idea of hand-rolling your heating. 'People don't want to roll newspapers up,' he says. 'That suits me. It's quicker than chopping firewood.'

Sam used to operate a tubular design engineering works, which is where he made this weighted clothes-line. It can be raised and lowered effortlessly with a quick spin of the wheel, and has a locking mechanism to prevent unwanted movement.

Kelly, Graeme & Chris

Sound and vision

As far as they know, only one other organisation anywhere in the world is currently doing what Kelly Waterman, Graeme Jones and Chris Lock are doing. That happens to be a company in the United Kingdom, which has invested massive amounts on planar, or flat speakers. Last November, in Las Vegas, the results of that expenditure were launched at the sprawling World Computer Show, Comdex. Kelly, Graeme and Chris saw the launch. They were there too, but with a much more modest exhibit — their Slab speaker. Kelly remembers the Brits' reaction. 'They didn't know about us. The reaction was, "What are the Kiwis doing here, with some technology made in the garden shed?" You could tell they were very nervous. They'd spent seventeen million pounds on R & D, and ours sounded better.'

That's a bold assertion, but it's backed by evidence that some of the largest companies on the planet are 'waiting for product'. Plane makers, computer makers, major money-makers are all lining up for a 'test drive'. And they're not looking at a replica of what's been developed in Britain, either. 'We're using different methods,' says Kelly, 'and different patents.' And they're producing different types of ultra-thin speaker as well. One of them is Graeme's invention. And, yes, it was developed in his garden shed.

Graeme's contribution, which Chris calls 'a stunning device', is an electrodynamic speaker. For the uninitiated, that means it works in much the same way as the boxes on either side of your CD player with the weird plastic front that makes it look like Darth Vadar before his face lift. An electrodynamic speaker uses coils and a magnet to create a magnetic field which, in turn, vibrates the speaker panel. And it's those vibrations we hear as mellifluous, melodic sound. (Or heavy metal.)

Graeme's been working on his design since 1992, when he started the search for 'a cost-effective panel' that would produce high-quality sound. And he's succeeded. His speakers 'are cheaper and simpler', says Kelly. 'Just operating in isolation, the standard Kiwi way, I developed something totally unique in the world.' Already, there's a second generation of his original speaker. 'The first generation was larger and had square edges,' says Graeme. 'Now it's thinner, smaller, and with improved performance. And we can make it thinner yet. We can get it down to the thickness of a piece of cardboard. And with no frame.'

Graeme, whose shed experiments began a process that could now well achieve international success.

Making sound waves right around the world, Kelly (left), Chris (centre) and Graeme (right) in the small plant where their speakers are evolving. A first generation Slab stands alone on the table at front left. A version with a visual treatment is just behind it. Right in front of the threesome are two second generation upright speakers (in grey) and one, even smaller, black horizontal model. With any luck, something very similar will be coming soon to a sound system, TV or computer near you.

What makes that even more amazing is that the speakers are bi-polar, meaning 'both sides of the speaker are working at once'.

The same goes for the second project. Not electrodynamic, but electrostatic, it's the result of research and experiments Kelly's been doing for years. Electrostatic speakers aren't new. But they've always been for the super-purist, because they're more expensive, he says. 'But we're using new technologies and new materials. We're taking the latest developments in electronics and computer modelling to optimise the system.'

Again, for the unlettered, electrostatic systems rely on a thin film or diaphragm sandwiched between high-voltage plates. Positive and negative charges 'move the film backwards and forwards in the electrical field. It's only very small distances but it's very accurate.' Again, the end result of all those small movements is the gentle stimulation of the tympanic membrane that produces sound. Electrostatic speakers are always likely to cost more than the electrodynamic alternative, but their sonic accuracy makes them first choice for the dedicated audiophile. That's more than enough to justify pressing on. Through the Graduate Research Industry Fellowship, or GRIF programme, Kelly's got a very smart young engineer also involved in testing, improving and getting it right. 'In New Zealand,' Kelly says, 'we've got to get into new technology quick, then innovate it and get it into the market.'

Make no mistake. This work is at the cutting edge. Graeme's invention in particular has huge potential. With flat-screen technology transforming

Another product for the sound fanatic, this is Kelly's Tube Valve Amplifier. 'It's a hybrid,' he says. It combines electronic control circuitry with valves 'since the old valves are still deemed to be superior to transistors'. Overseas equivalents can sell for as much as $100,000, although cheaper versions of this technology are also available. 'At $13,000, our unit's pretty competitive,' says Kelly.

television sets and computer monitors, 'there'll be no place for bulky speakers'. Of course, it goes without saying that it's been an expensive exercise. But this trio don't have £17 million on hand. Most of the research has been funded with money generated by Kelly's core business, repairing and recycling old speakers like Goodmans, Wharfdales and Altecs, 'The Voice of the Theatre'.

'To go into production you need money,' says Graeme. 'In that way, this country's not very helpful. Money's hard to get.' Kelly agrees. 'The idea's easy. Getting the capital to take a risk for six months to get it to market, that's the hard bit. If I wanted to import second-hand cars or open a massage parlour, no problem. But if I want to make something that someone like a bank manager doesn't understand, they just scratch their head. Sorry, it's too hard. It's not being done by anyone overseas.' And there are hurdles there too. 'There's a disbelief that New Zealand can do it,' Chris explains, 'and it's hard to get communication lines flowing. Big companies are so ponderous and the inertia is such that it takes a long time to do things.'

But they all agree there's something we've got that's been invaluable. Unprompted, they recognise the value of the shed. 'The ideal Kiwi workshop was always one where you stirred the tea with a broken hacksaw blade,' suggests Graeme. 'The success of a project depended on how many cups of tea you put into it,' adds Chris. All three think that tradition's under threat. 'We're reaching a problem now,' says Kelly. 'This generation coming through is not getting into sheds with their dads. Either they haven't got dads or everyone's too busy. Thirty years ago, if you wanted to make a hi-fi system, you usually started when Dad gave you the turntable he didn't want.' Graeme amplifies the point. 'When you made those things, you'd get instruction and help. This generation now, it's not practical at all. There's no basic understanding. There's a huge need for a lot of engineers now to train young people.' That sparks dissent. 'No! No!,' says Chris. 'Train the forty-year-olds, and we can train the young.'

That should keep them busy when the speakers are a global hit.

Kelly conducting tests on one of the electrostatic prototypes he's developing.

Arthur

Snags, fags, Lotto and locks

Two or three years back, Arthur was idly flicking through the daily paper. Given what he was about to spot, poetic licence should have had him happily ensconced at the time in the smallest room. But, as ever, the truth's more mundane. He was actually in the kitchen when he spied an article lauding the local 'inventors' of a self-raising (and lowering) loo seat. That's odd, thought Arthur as he quickly went to inspect his own ablutions and, in particular, the self-raising (and lowering) loo seat he'd designed and installed some months before. At the time, he felt it was something of rare and special promise. Until he discovered that several souls overseas had already had the same idea. His was merely the latest in a (relatively) long line of self-raising (and lowering) loo seats.

Hence Arthur's surprise to find numerous column inches of rhapsodic prose devoted to people who'd come up with something that had already been invented! He tells the story as a kind of summary of all the hours he's spent concocting inventions in his 'brooding shed' — not to be confused with his 'brewing shed', where something entirely different gets concocted. Arthur's the first to admit that he's had an unhappy tendency to invent the right thing at the wrong time or for the wrong people, or to lack the funds to turn a great prototype into a successful product.

Take the Cut Down, Arthur's invention for the reluctant smoker. The principle's straightforward. 'When you have a craving for nicotine,' the inventor explains, 'you don't need to smoke a whole cigarette—five puffs will satisfy your craving.' So, after the requisite number of puffs, 'you just place your lighted end in the Cut Down and it will extinguish itself in about five seconds.' The benefits are not inconsiderable, says Arthur. 'You halve the amount of cigarettes that you smoke, you halve the pollution to the environment and you reduce by 50 percent the nicotine and tar intake into your system.' Ah yes, but anyone who's ever trifled with tobacco will know how unpleasant it can be to relight what has been put out. Not so with the Cut Down, Arthur insists, 'because the cone of ash is retained . . . when you relight it, it doesn't have that harsh taste . . . it's like a fresh lit cigarette.' He was so sure of the Cut Down's potential he invested a lot of his own money to manufacture 5000. Unhappily, the Smoke Free legislation's made a lot of people nervous. Arthur says it's been hard getting his ads accepted. Which hasn't done much for the health of his bank account or the health of the nation's addicts. The Cut Down may not be politically correct, says Arthur, but he's convinced it's an effective, inexpensive way to wean one off the dreaded weed.

Another product that deserves to get off the ground is the Rod Holder, a nifty bit of kit which fits over a car window and looks after the rod while the angler looks after the hook, line and sinker. The Rod Holder is Arthur's answer to a persistent problem. 'Where do you put your rod?' he asks. 'If you lean it against the car it can fall on the ground, get dirt on it. Some people have

Arthur Sparrow, tireless inventor, who also featured in *Blokes and Sheds*.

This is Arthur's brooding shed, source of many inventive ideas.

Consisting of a hinged bracket and tube, the Rod Holder allows easy preparation of fishing lines.

thousand-dollar reels. You can't get the slightest bit of dust on gear like that. With this thing, everything's up off the ground.'

Somehow, news of this ingenious hands-free device reached the executive operators of an American television shopping channel. At an indecently early hour one morning, Arthur got a phone call from an enthusiastic shoperator who insisted the Rod Holder would be a sure-fire hit with US anglers, provided they knew about it. And provided Arthur could supply an initial order of 50,000. 'Well, I just didn't have the funds,' he says, 'the production and tooling costs were huge. I simply couldn't afford it.'

So the Rod Holder's languished, its potential unfulfilled. Arthur makes them on request, of course, but not in the numbers he'd originally hoped. He's had similar problems with the Snag Away, an effective lightweight float sent down the line to free snared hooks from vexatious boulders and obstacles. Arthur ruefully concedes a brief promotional campaign on a regional television channel was 'probably aimed at the wrong audience', but he's still optimistic about the future of his fishing aids.

The same goes for his locks. His efforts to find the definitive fastener began when 'a lady friend' asked if he could design an effective, childproof lock. He's produced a number of prototypes since then, including a push-button gate clasp that can be released by pressure from shoulder or elbow, 'when you've got your hands full with grocery bags and the like'. Arthur showed one of his childproof locks to a friend in the police force. 'He was impressed and he said I should do something about it. So I did. And I think I got ripped off.'

Challenged to act, Arthur contacted a manufacturer of security equipment. A meeting was arranged and his prototype taken away for further assessment. Some considerable time later, 'I got a letter saying "Thanks very much, Arthur, but we won't be putting your lock into production. We've got a very similar design being developed at the moment." So I thought, "Stuff you. I'll invent a childproof lock that's the most super-duper ever—something that you've never seen."'

This is Arthur's invention to help the devotees of specific Lotto digits. With this, Arthur says he can check how well he's done in less than 45 seconds. A card with his numbers underlined is slipped into the frame. Then he drops little buttons into the holes as the balls fall. At the end of the draw, a quick check to see how many underlined numbers are still visible tells him how well he's done.

An ashtray with added extras, the Cut Down could double the life of a pack of cigarettes.

And that's what he's working on now, spending hours in his shed to perfect a design he's convinced will be better than anything else available, something the world will clamour for. Arthur's determined to make this one work. And to make this one succeed. If there's any justice, that's exactly what will happen.

The push-action gate — the button on the right-hand side allows easy opening.

A prototype of one of Arthur's childproof locks.

Ian
Finding room for a spin

As sections contract and town houses expand, more and more ordinary ursons (urban persons) are waking up to the fact that something's missing. Not infrequently, it's room for the car. And, as more and more affluent ursons colonise bluff and crag in pursuit of a vista, they too are discovering that what their mortgage has actually paid for is a view with no room.

What to do? Where to put the motor (or motors) when there's but a car's length and five additional inches between the garage door and the neighbour's fence? How to manoeuvre your Benz, your frenz' Benz and the dinky wee Daihatsu on a site where the swinging of a cat would require a resource consent?

Confronted with the restraints of a micro-site, or the vertiginous slopes of a windswept peak, the sensible urson would probably go straight into a flat spin. But only if they had something like the CARousel on the estates. It's Ian Webb's answer to the growing problem of shrinking space. And before the jaundiced reader indignantly declares that car turntables aren't new, let's examine it more carefully.

The shed in which Ian's inventions have their genesis. One such design is a barbeque table with a centrally mounted 'lazy Susan'. 'You can get fourteen people around it,' he says, 'and no one has to pass anything. It's the only one of its kind in the country. Ian's gearing up for production now and hopes to sell the table as a kitset. 'You could have it together in half an hour,' he says. He estimates the full retail price would be $3,000.

The CARousel turntable can be installed inside or out. A unit costs about $16,000 but, as Ian points out, if you are desperate for space on a small section then it is a necessity. And, 'on a million-dollar property, it's absolutely nothing'.

The motor, gearbox and driving wheel. The unit's spring-loaded so that it's constantly held, under pressure, against the rim of the Carousel. A rolled section of angle iron prevents vertical movement.

In some ways, the CARousel reveals something quite important about the nature of invention. Because, while it may be true that it's not be a new thing, it is a thing done in a new way. And most inventions are the same. The concept may not be novel, but the method is. That's certainly the case here. For a start, this turntable uses 'a cantilever system', about which Ian is understandably guarded. But the key feature is that although there are no parts on the outside, it'll take 2 tonne. 'When I first thought of the idea, the engineers said "No way." They were supposed to be the experts, so I tried other solutions. But I ended up doing it my way. The hub is the key. It's the crucial part, the real invention.'

If the hub's a critical part of load support, propulsion's provided elsewhere. Although not essential, CARousels are generally spun by a small electric motor — 'A quarter-horse will do it,' says Ian. The motor, with an attached gearbox, is mounted in a recess alongside the turntable and drives a small, horizontally mounted wheel. The unit is remotely controlled with a little two-button gizmo that goes on a key ring. 'It can lock up your garage door as well,' Ian adds helpfully. In addition, you can operate it from a back-up, wall-mounted control box.

There are, as there should be in these enlightened times, alternative energy sources available. 'A pre-schooler can push a car around,' says Ian. 'A lot of people don't put a motor in. The thing is, it's incredible for space.' Take the case of the person with 'five inches between the car and the fence. It allows room to turn. In fact, [this person] only got permission to build because they put one of these in.'

So far, Ian's sold about seventy: 'One in Tahiti, which was nice, and seven or eight in Australia. People say they're happy with them, they're so durable.' He acknowledges he 'could make it lighter, put wheels on the outside, but every one is a potential source of trouble. I'm a practical person, I hate going back to fix things. My plan was to eliminate trouble — make it foolproof.' In that, he's succeeded. And, after a quiet period when demand was limited, to say the least, orders are starting to come in. Not bad for a bloke who defied the engineers, backed his own hunch, built the first CARousel on his own, in his shed, then sold his house to fund the commercial development of his 'revolutionary' invention.

Geoff

A good deal from A to Zed

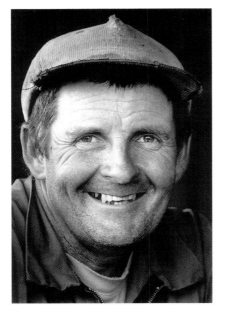

**Geoff's a real sheddie's
sheddie.**

Back for an encore is Geoff Deal, who made a spectacular appearance in *Blokes and Sheds*. A dedicated sheddie, and owner of a magnificent wilderness, Geoff's always asserted he could find anything in the rubble in less than a minute. When he was put to the test, as part of the exhaustive research for that earlier volume, he found the three-sided widget, or whatever it was, with seconds to spare. But his ability to find that which can't easily be detected isn't limited to obscure and dusty items. He's pretty good at finding solutions as well.

Take these two very different inventions. One is a clever little uni-pole swing. If there's not room for a standard model, or unwelcome excavations are needed to put the supports in place, then Geoff's add-on alternative might be the answer. It just bolts on to the clothes-line, flag pole, cellphone mast or anything else that's vertical and handy. And should the clothes-line, or whatever, be square and not round, then the fitting can easily be adapted accordingly. The swing does everything its larger counterpart does, without taking up anywhere near as much space.

The other idea is more to do with straying than playing. Temporary tape fencing is a common feature on New Zealand farms these days. It can be electrified in order to shield a particular area or to stop stock heading off in the wrong direction. What Geoff's done is invent a way to easily electrify a temporary fence, then just as easily disconnect the current. What he's created is a little gizmo he's called the Zed Connector. Not too surprising, given that its shape so closely resembles the letter of the alphabet. For a reason.

'It's all to do with the surface area of the contact,' Geoff explains. 'The actual shape is very important. It took a lot of work to get it right.' It was burn-out that led him to develop the idea in the first place. The common way to electrify a temporary fence is to use spring clips. But Geoff's found 'spring clips tend to burn the tapes out. They've only got tiny stainless steel wires inside.'

Never one to limit himself, Geoff's actually been working at both ends of the alphabet, so to speak. Not only has he got the Zed Connector, he's also got an ABC — A Beaut Cowshed. With the shed, which he built himself, now up and running, the Connectors have helped bewildered bovines navigate unfamiliar territory. They've also impressed the odd neighbour who has happened to spot them and, with the idea protected, Geoff has plans to develop it commercially. One thing's for sure, if it gives him an excuse to spend more time in the shed shed, he'll be on the job tomorrow.

Hanna on the uni-swing with Cortney and Eleta doing the pushing.

The uni-swing attachment can be altered to suit the profile of the pole.

The Zed Connector uses one spring clip to link a permanent electric fence and the temporary tape. The clip can be removed when current's not required.

Roy
Making water work

A quote from Albert Einstein hangs on the wall of Roy Martin's shed. The cardboard's a bit dusty but the message is clear: 'Imagination is of far greater value than knowledge'. Roy proves the point really. Over the years, he's repeatedly used his imagination to invent a lot of good and novel things. Things that challenge the conventional wisdom. Things that work. And since he used to be a plumber, until the lingering effects of a serious war wound forced him to give up the business, it's probably not surprising that many of his inventions harness the potential of water.

As a 'full-time inventor', Roy says he doesn't worry too much about the financial returns. 'I'm disabled, all war injuries, so I think of things. Then I go down to the factory and see people making them, and they're all part of the team. It's not just me. I do the prototypes, they do the rest. You can't do nothing on your own.'

One of his earliest ideas was a water turbine, which he originally called the Plata Pump. It won him an award as Inventor of the Year, picked up prizes at the Australian Field Days and even featured on the BBC. 'My brother saw me,' says Roy. 'It was on stations all around the world.' Strangely enough, having built the turbine himself, he very nearly gave the project up when the initial tests were less than successful. Dropped into a swollen stream, the turbine's blades sputtered rather than spun. 'It was only doing two revolutions a minute.' Dejected, Roy went home. 'But the next day, going back, I could hear a noise like a motor. It was the turbine. The stream had dropped and it was doing four hundred revs a minute.'

Unfortunately, although he's had turbines pumping water 150 feet up a hill, Roy says academic reaction's been lukewarm. At best. The boffins, he says, dismiss turbines as inefficient. And maybe they are, he says. But that's not the point. 'They're still better than carrying water in baskets.' Besides, 'What about the car? That's one of the most inefficient motors that man's ever made. And we still use it.' So he's continued to refine and expand his turbine range. One new idea is a very small water turbine that fits inside the downpipe of a house so that, every time it rains, 'the downpipe is a penstock in a miniature way. And you can use the turbine in the downpipe to pump water to a tank.'

Roy's also developed a range of sealed turbines. These need a much smaller quantity of water passing through them than the open ones require. But they

A selection of closed turbines (centre and right) in Roy's shed. In the left foreground is one of his small spherical Floating Reservoirs.

need to be located 'low down or use a fall in a stream' because water has to drop 'from about a metre' into the turbines to have them operate effectively. Not only can these pump water, they can also generate electricity. 'A chap from the Argentine has taken three of these turbines and used them to put electric light in approximately fifty houses, a church and a school.'

Another new and aquatic invention is Roy's Floating Reservoir. How this works is top secret, the subject of a world patent. But what it does is 'turn dirty water into clean water'. Available as spheres or in a larger, 'box' form, the reservoirs are designed to be placed in a stream or river, 'connected to the bank with a pipe'. Water from the reservoir would be 'pumped by hand in India and

The 'paddle steamer' blades are an obvious feature of the open turbine.

elsewhere', says Roy, adding that 'there is UN interest in this one'. His original idea was to provide clean water for cattle. 'Some streams are so dirty farmers won't let their cattle drink out of them.' But now Roy says he's sure he can get water fit for people too. 'I don't think it's going to be any problem.'

Occasionally, Roy comes ashore as well. One of his niftiest inventions is so popular it keeps getting borrowed by friends and neighbours. It's a patented adjustable device that fits on the bottom of a ladder to allow it to stand straight on sloping ground. Called the Ladder Jack, it's a classic 'Why didn't I think of that' idea and the sooner it turns up in hardware stores and builders' merchants the better.

Then there's his latest creation, that might save the allegedly cash-strapped health system a tidy sum. Since 'thousands of people need special beds' and since 'they can cost up to $5,000', Roy's produced an inexpensive alternative. Not a bed, but a headrest unit that fits to a bed. 'I could've made it hydraulic,' says Roy, 'but that would have added complexity and cost. And you don't need that. There's a handle on each side, they're easy to operate, it's easy to alter the height if someone's sick in bed.' And it only costs $250! 'It's a simple thing,' Roy says. 'I'm not capable of doing complicated things. That's the way I look at things. That's what inventions are all about — simplicity.'

And stamina. Because Roy's had his share of setbacks and disappointments. In a totally rational world, a lot of his inventions would have enjoyed more success. But he keeps going. 'People say to me, "Roy, you never give up." I say, "Why should I?" It's not our spirit, is it? New Zealanders are such innovative people. There are ideas everywhere. It's just marvellous.'

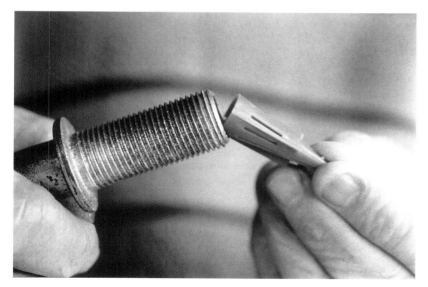

An invention that stems from Roy's plumbing background, this is the Pyramid Valve Filter. It fits into a ballcock and stops it blocking up.

Jack & Jo

A new way to move

Inventor Jack Shuttleworth, with designer Jo Rainey behind. They haven't always had the hi-tech assistance they can call on now. 'When we make an engine now,' says Jo, 'it's designed by a computer. So it fits together first time and will run first time and will produce the power we predicted very accurately. The greatest problem for Jack was envisaging parts, and fitting and shaping them. It was a huge, huge task.'

A hundred years of use and investment is a huge hurdle to overcome. A hundred years of refinement and improvement inevitably produces a good and durable product. Something that works well, that people are familiar with, feel secure about and are equipped to fix, should the need arise. That's undeniably the case with the engine in your car. Some of the world's largest corporations have spent billions of dollars on enhancements. The result, as Jo Rainey himself concedes, is 'fuel economy, reliability, emissions and cost . . . we could only dream of fifty years ago'. That would seem to be a classic case of something that ain't broke and don't need fixing. When you add the natural reluctance of companies and customers to flirt with the unproven, why would anyone want to challenge the dominance of the four-stroke, reciprocating piston engine?

Ah, well, that's because it's a bit like the typewriter keyboard really. If you were starting with a clean sheet of paper today, you'd probably do both of them differently. For instance, that much maligned item, the keyboard, would not be designed around a sales gimmick. Have a close look at yours next time you're pounding it. Note how the top line contains all the letters needed to rapidly belt out the magic word 'typewriter'. Long before OOS played its hand, that was an invaluable tool for salespersons seeking to sell the new and unfamiliar technology.

Likewise, if you were designing a propulsion system for cars today, it wouldn't be a four-stroke. According to Jo, the dictates of efficiency would determine that you went 'for the power-to-weight ratio and low emission levels of a properly designed two-stroke engine'.

That's exactly what Jack Shuttleworth did back in the days when he used to race boats. 'I started in 1988, with petrol engines,' he says. 'I did my 228 ks or whatever it was then, with a young family. I had to give it up.' But not before he'd started experimenting with engines of his own. 'I didn't look at any books or anything,' he recalls. Even so, his first design was a 7-litre, 5-cylinder, petrol-driven motor with 'Caterpillar D6 bulldozer pistons' for his hydroplane. After building a second engine, 'I went off petrol. I realised I could make a make a diesel compression ignition engine so much lighter in actual format that what was being done.' His first diesel was a little single-cylinder built in 1996. A larger 3-litre, 5-cylinder engine followed.

Throughout the course of his endeavours, there were problems of one sort or another. Jack's wife, Jenny, remembers getting so frustrated in the boating days when they had little kids and no money that, one night, she took drastic action. Jack had gone out somewhere in spite of her declaration, 'You do and you'll be sorry.' Indeed he was. In the dead of night, Jenny went out to the shed, 'lifted the block off the bench, wrapped a sack round it and buried it'. Jack eventually got it back, but not before certain faithful promises had been made. Later, when he was building and testing his engine designs, 'there were bits of aluminium flying out of that shed'. On several occasions, Jenny recalls, 'I'd

Conducting a static test, Jack (kneeling) makes a minor adjustment, watched by Jo (left) and Ramon Brown (rear) from Canterbury University. The University's now conducting a mechanical evaluation of the engine.

hear a big whoomf, and I knew it was a fire. I'd stand and wait for another sound, thinking "Is he alive?" The neighbours were the same. When they heard the banging start, that meant he was alive.'

Not only alive but still at work on what were actually a series of axial engine designs. An axial engine is one in which the pistons and output shaft run in a parallel plane, rather than at right angles as is the case with a conventional motor. And, although Jack's engines use 'standard pistons and cylinders', they're arranged in a ring and not in a line. Normally, pistons spin a crankshaft as they go up and down. With Jack's design, the pistons 'drive the output shaft through a system similar to a Z-crank'.

Soon after Jack finished his second diesel he and Jo, an industrial designer, decided to develop the engine commercially. It had obvious advantages. 'It's a very simple engine, small and compact and very low-cost,' Jo says. 'It has a reasonable fuel efficiency, and the emissions will satisfy the current regulations, and they're really tough. It's also got multi-fuel capabilities for the future.'

Supported by a local investor, the duo have already produced a demonstration engine, a 2.5-litre, 5-cylinder, two-stroke diesel. 'It's got the same power and torque as a Commodore V6,' says Jo, 'but the V6 weighs twice as much and is twice as big. It's a hundred kilos for the Shuttleworth, two hundred for the V6.' Despite those advantages, they're proceeding cautiously. 'It will have applications in cars, but the problems of taking on the car industry are huge. So initially,' Jo says, 'we'll be looking at niches that are small enough to cope with.' He thinks the first application will be a marine inboard running a stern drive or water jet. 'There's a reasonable market size

A distinctive barrel shape, the latest 2.5-litre, 5-cylinder engine (left) sits beside an earlier version of the design. Having no valves, rockers or camshafts helps make the engine light, as does the built-in turbocharger. But Jack believes further refinement can get total weight down from 100 to 70 kg.

The axial nature of the design's clearly apparent here, with the five piston cylinders parallel to the output shaft. The first axial designs, including a Bristol aero-engine, appeared in the early years of the 20th century, but Jack didn't know anyone else had done it when he began work on his engine.

and it's relatively simple to put into a boat. The other application is as an aircraft engine', but because that's a tough market to break into 'it's not something we'll do overnight'.

A promising development has been an association with a small but innovative American company with its own revolutionary idea. Namely, an ignition and injection system which doesn't need a spark plug and, in fact, makes it entirely redundant. Applying that technology to this engine will not only help to showcase both but also improve fuel efficiency and further reduce weight. To ensure they stay on the right track, Jo and Jack have had academics here and overseas review progress regularly. One of their advisors is a Belfast academic who's the world authority on two-strokes. 'We want people like that to tell us what the problems are, so we can shut down if it's a waste of money.' So far, that hasn't seemed necessary, although there's quite a lot of work to do yet, says Jo. 'We're lucky. We've got a good investor behind us. Most New Zealand inventions come from back-yard inventors with back-yard budgets.'

The next stage will be to make five prototypes for exhaustive testing. And, within a year, there'll be some very nice pre-production engines running in demonstrable conditions. 'Come back and you'll be able to have a hurtle round in a jet boat,' says Jo. 'We'll make twenty and give them to jet boat clubs and let them thrash them, and break them, then refine and improve some more.' He believes those improvements can and should be done here.

'We're very good at engines in this country. We've got a wide knowledge of engine development processes. We've got the motivation and the costs are excellent compared with the US and Europe. There are guys living round here who've been working for Formula One teams, turbocharger experts, an expert engine prototype parts caster, who lives on an orchard and does beautiful work. I really, really want to do this here.' Not least because Jo believes we've got a major confidence problem in this country, especially amongst men. 'New Zealanders don't realise how marvellous we are. Maybe this will help. Because this is one back-yard invention that's going to be a world success.'

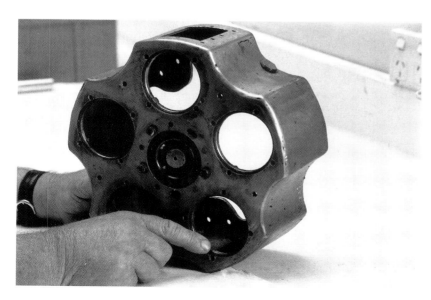

Computer modelling means a new or modified part now requires very little pattern making. 'With rapid prototyping we get a 3D model and it's squirted out,' says Jo. 'Two years ago, that was a dream. Now it's available on a PC at home.'

Asmeet
Not just another brick in the wall

Asmeet's eco-brick earned her awards from Zonta, the Regional Council and the title 'Young Environmentalist of the Year'.

As a general rule, fourteen-year-olds are not big on bricks. Kicks, yes. Flicks, yes. But bricks, no. Pink Floyd put the mockers on bricks really. It's just that no one told Asmeet. She was the exception to the rule. When she was fourteen she set out to find a way to make a better brick, in a way that nobody had tried before. A way that sought to take what we waste and put it to constructive use.

It was exactly the sort of task she'd been setting herself ever since the day she first entered a Science Fair. That was back in Standard Two, when Asmeet seriously began trying to make new things out of rubbish and things she found. 'A lot of things at home never get used, old machinery, rubbish, scrap paper, bits and pieces or whatever and I'd just start fiddling around.'

The inspiration for the bricks came from the TV show, 'Beyond 2000'. Asmeet saw an item about 'someone who made a house out of hay bales with clay poured on top. It was in a country where they had heaps of hay left over and it was a good house for insulation.' Deciding that she'd adopt the idea here, she found that clay was 'quite expensive and not a good resource'. But there were equivalents. One obvious one was waste paper, another was sawdust. Asmeet decided that they'd be for her what hay had been for the builders she'd seen.

So she set to in the shed to do the hard work. 'My dad helped me a little bit, he helped me build the mould, the wooden mould for the bricks.' After that she got stuck in 'on the floor' and mixed up all the ingredients. 'I quite liked doing it,' she says, 'getting in there on my hands and knees and all that stuff.' For the next two years, she spent most of her time in the shed. Getting the right mixture to go into the moulds was a long process of trial and error. The first bricks Asmeet made did not perform perfectly in field trials. She left a test batch outside for a year, only to find they'd 'started to crumble round the edges. The ratios of sawdust and paper are critical.'

Eventually she found the right combination of sawdust and paper, blended with cement 'and some other secret ingredients to hold it together'. That gave her bricks about the same weight as a standard red one, bricks that also produced good results for insulation, fire resistance and durability, although she's still fine-tuning to improve performance 'before putting it out on the market'.

That may take some time. Seventeen now, Asmeet's concentrating on her seventh form studies. She's hoping to get back to the bricks once exams and the like are out of the way. She wants to do more detailed and exhaustive research and may look for 'some financial assistance' to perfect her invention. In time, perchance, to have it help pay off her student loan. Meanwhile, she's still entering Science Fairs and is working on another ecologically sound prototype. A joint venture with her sister, it's a chimney filter to 'help the problem with the smog'. Between them, they've built a model which features a filter mechanism and a fan. The fan 'draws particles up through the filter' where they're trapped before being released into the air.

The next stage will be construction of a full-sized version, although Asmeet concedes 'it'll be quite hard to build in the shed'.

That's not likely to deter her. 'I just like fiddling around and making new stuff. I enjoy finding solutions to things and all the little problems I have along the way. The things that come up that I have to fix. I guess I'm quite a determined person, really. I like achieving my goals.'

The eco-brick. A search of the Internet convinced Asmeet that waste paper was ideal for her project. 'We've got heaps and heaps piled up. If we don't do something like this the rubbish dumps will just keep increasing in size.'

The perfect place for 'fiddling around'. Asmeet spent long hours on her hands and knees mixing different combinations of paper, sawdust and cement. 'At times it was a bit cold,' she says.

Murray

An open and shut case

'There must be something in the water here that gives you the inventing thing,' says Murray Prattley. As a long-time inventor himself, and someone who built a successful company around a range of innovative farming products, he's probably better equipped than most to judge. Although he's retired now, he's still at it, even if it does cause the odd spot of bother. 'One of the neighbours has just come over,' he reports, with a twinkle in his eye. 'He thought there might be a crime wave or something. He said, "You haven't seen a bloody gate, have you?"' Murray chuckles. 'I pointed over there and said, "Is that it?"'

And it was. Murray had temporarily 'acquired' the gate in order to test his latest invention. It's something the neighbour may enjoy using when it's finally developed. What Murray's designed is a detachable unit that can be fitted to a gate so that it can be opened and closed with a remote. It's the driveway or paddock equivalent of an automatic garage door except that, since it's not permanently attached, it can be moved from gate to gate as the need arises.

It was a deer farmer who got him started on the project, which he says 'just brings automatic gates into the electronic age'. Frustrated by certain exigencies of his operation, the farmer bent Murray's ear. 'He said, "You're supposed to be a clever bugger. Why the hell don't you invent a farm gate I

Getting it right. Murray contemplates various versions of his invention. The final design is the one he's holding. Contacts in the United States have seen it and 'they just can't wait till they get it'.

don't have to get off the tractor to open?" He said he was on and off the old John Deere forty times a day. So, forty times a day, there was the chance of breaking his ankle or running over himself.'

Fired with a determination to avoid that occurrence, Murray set to work. He looked at various options, including gates activated by water, but found 'that was not too effective in areas where there are frosts'. Other methods left a gate 'hard to open and close in a high wind'. In the end, because different gates on a farm are used at different times, he decided the solution had to be portable. 'No one else can do that. That's its main selling feature.' And, speaking of selling, if or when the invention reaches the market, Murray says it will be in the $400 to $500 price range, about the same you pay for a garage door opener.

For that, a purchaser would get a unit that could be 'operated by remote, or by a button on the unit, or manually if all else fails'. Murray's built in that third option for two reasons. One is that the unit's likely to run off a battery, and there's always a chance it will fail. The other is Murray second-guessing his customers. 'A farmer will put everything in your road. You've got to find an answer for him before he finds a fault.' So, in case it has occurred that a battery might get nicked, Murray's covered that as well. 'It'll be built-in, with a lock on it,' he says, 'or we might use a solar panel on the device.' As for the motor that will drive the wheel, 'all I intend to put in', he says, 'is an ordinary twelve-volt car windscreen wiper motor. I've tested it. That's all it needs.'

Sorting it all out has involved many trials and errors. 'If you could've seen the silly things I've done to get to this stage,' he laughs, 'you'd just shake your head. But that's the way it goes. For every successful thing you've got going, there are ten models behind the door that don't work.' He's increasingly confident this one will. 'At least I've persisted. I want the satisfaction of saying, "I think I did this one myself." In the end, the answer to everything is a simpler version. Anything complicated doesn't work.'

The unit in position, attached to a gate. Being detachable allows it to be moved around heavy-use areas on a farm or other property.

Another view of Murray's invention. It's designed to be height-adjustable and is spring-loaded 'to keep pressure off the wheel a bit'. A young friend and computer whiz has helped with the microswitches. For security reasons, there's a unit-specific remote and a clutch for manual operation 'under extreme circumstances'.

Laurie

From singing to spouting

In the orchestrated litany of misery that we tolerate as news, most catastrophies and scandals have a life expectancy of an adult dragonfly. But some calamities do manage to make a lasting impression. That unhappy omen of a dehydrated future, the great Auckland water shortage of 1996 is one such. It certainly had a profound effect on Laurie, and an equally positive effect on his inventing career. 'That's where I came from,' says Laurie. 'It all started with that water shortage.' The search for a solution to a crisis he felt was 'largely man-made' took him back to the classroom. 'At school, I'd studied agriculture,

A familiar face, Laurie says his father always wanted him to take up engineering. Instead, he opted for showbiz, featuring as a singer on TV shows such as 'Happen Inn' and 'Free Ride'. He also worked with Billy T. James on 'Radio Times', before getting back to engineering and the go-go world of invention.

not that it did me a hell of a lot of good. But I knew how much water came off a roof.'

Rather than see it 'go down the plughole', he invented the Downpipe Tap. The name says it all, really. The Tap's a water diverter fitted to a downpipe and used in conjunction with a storage tank. It has an external outlet which diverts rainwater to a tank, and a second, internal, fitting which automatically cuts that supply when the tank's full. Designed to slide easily into a downpipe (once it's been cut) the Tap could be installed in about fifteen minutes. 'They started off with a hiss and a roar,' says Laurie, 'until the crisis was over, then they died down.'

But not before they'd triggered a second invention. For the Taps to work efficiently, a good water flow was needed. Blocked or constricted downpipes prevented that happening. Laurie put his mind to the problem, which usually started in the spouting. 'Most gutter guards rely on slots, or holes,' he says. 'If you've got a small hole, it blocks in heavy rain. If you've got a big hole, it won't stop the rubbish. You need a hole that's big and small at the same time.' And he found it, in a most unusual place. 'I was inspired by a toilet brush.'

What Laurie realised was that the bristles act like a maze. 'The further in, the denser the bristles. Anything that migrates through it, can't travel.' From that insight, he developed the Hedgehog gutter protection system. The prototype was, in fact, a toilet brush trimmed flat on one side. He's found it not only deals

The Hedgehog gutter protection system in place above a downpipe. Designed to be modular and easy to clean, Hedgehogs are still trimmed flat on one side by a modified shearing cone. Laurie says the largest manufacturer of twisted wire brushware in the US is 'very interested in making these for the American market'.

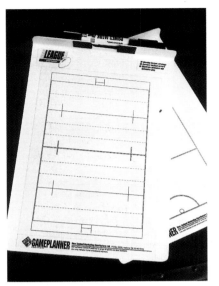

The clipboard whiteboard is one invention Laurie has put on the back burner for the time being, even though there would appear to be a number of teams that could benefit from its use. Complete with two pens and a magnetic duster, the board's marked to reproduce the layout of playing fields and courts used by various codes, so that coaches can give instant, and detailed, instructions to their players. After the unhappy performance of the 1998 Vincibles, this could just be John Hart's secret weapon at the World Cup.

with debris, but is also 'ideal for stopping birds getting under the roof. They don't like their private little places getting poked with this stuff.'

Like the Downpipe Tap, the Hedgehog was developed in the little shed at Laurie's place. He's got bigger premises now, because the Hedgehog took off. 'I've just launched it in Australia, it's going well. There's a big market in Queensland.' And, potentially, in the United States. Last year Laurie took a very deep breath, hopped on a plane and exhibited the Hedgehog at the Chicago Hardware Show, the largest of its kind in the world. The venture was very nearly a disaster. He'd made a model, of course, carefully constructed, with a pristine corrugated iron roof. The Americans couldn't believe that such a curious material went on the top of houses. That incongruity threatened acceptance of his idea. But a frantic dash around 24-hour hardware stores at 3 a.m. on the day the show opened enabled him to get the bits to simulate a more acceptable roofing material. The rest, as they say, is history. 'There was a very positive reaction,' says Laurie. 'We got some of the biggest crowds of any exhibitor there. It's an international problem, and no one's tackled it this way before.'

Don't make a bloody mess of your hands cleaning the gutter...

...get a Hedgehog Gutter Brush!

The only gutter brush available with nylon bristles, galvanised twist-wire spine and polypropylene handle.

It's hard to pick holes in a gutter filter that doesn't have any...

...get a Hedgehog Gutter Filter!

Filters pine needles and other hard to capture debris. Easy to fit. Easy to clean.

© 1995 Laurie Dee Patents Pending

Laurie now has two Hedgehog products on the market — the filter and a gutter brush.

Tackling things in a different way is something Laurie enjoys. 'I love inventing things. The biggest problem is, I don't stop. As soon as somebody says, "Can you do this?" I'm away. For a while, I'll think it's the greatest thing since sliced bread. But inventing's the easy part. The hardest part is marketing. With inventions, you've got to put so much money into it. Sometimes you just need to say, no, go and invent something else.'

And, although he probably doesn't have to, that's exactly what he's doing. As well as filling a growing order book, especially, at present, for the Hedgehog. Moving round the large workshop/warehouse he now operates from, Laurie picks up one of his bristly little creations. 'They say Kiwis can do anything with number eight wire,' he says with a grin. 'Well, this proves it. It's the ultimate number eight wire invention.'

The Downpipe Tap can be easily installed. A piece of paper wrapped round the pipe is the best way to get a straight line cut. After that, the unit's slipped in but not glued so it can be quickly removed for cleaning. The external outlet leading to the tank is at the base and the overflow outlet — inside the unit — is above it.

A recent invention for baches and farmhouses, this is the Rainwater Restorer. Normally mounted on the side of a water tank, the Restorer has an internal holding sump and filter. Water leaving the sump must pass through the filter, which screens most of the gunk before it reaches the tank. That means less cleaning, and reduced filtering costs and better tasting, healthier drinking water.

Clint & Al

Just call us inventerprenuers

Board games may not be the essence of cool in Nintendoland, but Monopoly, Scrabble, Ludo and the like continue nevertheless to flourish, the persistently popular choice of thousands. And now, thanks to Al Lester and Clint McInnes, Cricket Wizard's come to the crease to join that list of games people still play. Oddly enough, what got the game going wasn't a desire to have fun, but rather a deeply felt frustration. 'I was sick of listening to cricket on the radio and not knowing all those weird terms,' says Clint. 'I'd listen to some twit saying someone had whacked the ball out to third man and I'd think, "Where the bloody hell's third man?" I didn't have a clue.' Assuming there were others as perplexed as he was, Clint thought a game which educated and entertained might just be the answer. And, he says, 'I was sick to death of having ideas and doing nothing about it, so I thought "Oh bugger it, I can't take my money to the grave" and decided to have a go.'

Over the next six months, on 'a number of hunting, shooting and fishing trips', he and Al debated the idea exhaustively. 'We've been friends for a long time,' says Al. They complement each other perfectly. 'Al's the logic side of the equation, I'm throwing rocks at the sun,' says Clint. Or, to put that Al's way, 'Clint's the ideas man. It's my job to make them work.' The breakthrough came on a trip to the Marlborough Sounds. Clint was in the throes of a male menopause thing. 'I wanted to build something from the tree up.' And Al, 'like a real mate, was trying to help him through it'.

It was winter, and they were building a generator shed. One night, working in the dark and frustrated building by Braille, they knocked off. 'Clint got his dice, because that's what the game was then, and said, "Do you want a game of cricket?" So we played and he asked what did I think and I said it was bloody

Al Lester: 'We've got some credibility now. We're not all wind and whistle. We've got a product, this is us.'

Clint McInnes: 'You've got to have a bit of fun. You either do it for fun or money.'

awful.' That triggered a vigorous debate. They sat up all night, thrashing out how the game should work. 'We realised we had to have a field,' says Al. 'So we ripped up bed rolls and drew up the field on them. We used matches to mark out the fielding positions.' And before it was time to get back to building, they'd hit on the vital ingredient.

'We struck on the fact we could actually replicate the percentages of what happens in a game with multi-sided dice,' Clint says. With a bowling dice, batting dice, a fielding dice, run dice and one for the third umpire, they could capture all the options one-day cricket can offer, with 'an element of skill and an element of chance'. Things moved quickly after that. They patented their multi-sided dice design and took the idea to some of the big games companies, 'who promptly ignored us', says Al. 'We thought they'd be clamouring to buy it off us,' Clint adds, 'and we'd take the royalty and retire.' When it became clear this wasn't going to happen, they decided to do the whole lot themselves.

A nineteen-page rule book was drawn up. 'We sent that away for field research,' says Al. 'And it came back with one word — bullshit,' continues Clint, 'so we went to visual.'

They hired a consultant, and sought advice from the Business Development Board. Clint taught himself 'graphics on the computer' and various packaging designs were prepared. Their research had already indicated significant international possibilities. 'Al's philosophy, the thing that kept him focused,

Al and Clint with their bedroll prototype. Clint describes them as a couple of 'inventerprenuers' — a word he is determined to see enter the English language.

was the idea that we were the boys from the back shed taking on the world,' says Clint. 'I found out some amazing things,' adds Al. 'Do you know the biggest middle class in the world? It's in India. They've got 900 million altogether and there are 400 million middle-class Indians. And they're all cricket mad.' That meant a large potential market. In addition, they estimated sales in New Zealand of 5000 games, plus 20,000 in Australia and as many as 50,000 in the UK.

Paradoxically, as they weighed up their options, Clint and Al saw computers as a potential ally. 'Computers are selfish,' says Clint. 'There's no interaction with a computer. Board games and cards are things parents can do to create interaction. Kids want that. They'll always gravitate back to physical, outdoor things or interaction with other people.' New Zealand Cricket was prepared to back the game. They could see it promoting cricket and serving as a valuable coaching aid.

Panels recruited to play the game said only Monopoly, Trivial Pursuits and Pictionary were more enjoyable, and 'women loved beating the blokes', says Al.

So they bit the bullet and, with help from the Business Development Board, funded an initial production run of 5000. Everything but the dice, 'which no one here could do', was made in New Zealand. The design and packaging was aimed at the top end of the market, says Clint. 'The things our country can compete in are quality and niche markets.' The early response has pleased Al. 'We sold 2400 in the first three months,' he says. Publicity overseas has drawn orders from Britain, the United States, Canada, Spain, the Netherlands 'and a whole heap of other countries'.

Even though the game's taking off, they've both got some sage advice for other inventors. 'The idea is the cheapest part you'll ever have. The lesson for all inventors is, if you think it's going to cost you a figure, then triple it and double it again.' They also advise a bit of scepticism and a lot of perseverance. 'When you're doing something like this, you trip over a lot of fly-by-nighters. For every hundred entrepreneurs in New Zealand, eighty percent stand around the bar talking about it, ten percent can't do it and one percent can. And, of that one

Ready to play, the Cricket Wizard board game numbers positions on the field and identifies them by name around the border. The game uses five dice and has proved unexpectedly popular with teenagers, who weren't considered likely fans. A Pocket Cricket version is now being developed.

percent, eighty percent will go broke in the first two years. That's about it.'

Well, not quite. The last word belongs to Al. 'An overnight success takes ten years of hard work. And we're only two years into it. Credibility's what you're selling at the end of the day. And we've got to maintain that right down the line. If we don't, it's all over. I mean, we're just a couple of family men and we've got to keep feeding the soldiers.'

The duo are now developing a game with NASA called Shuttle Wizard. It's a space shuttle game in which players have to build a space station. The game's launch will coincide with NASA's plans to build an actual space station, which will ensure a lot of news coverage while the game's on sale.

One of the cards for Shuttle Wizard. Clint and Al's children, and their friends, have been the models.

The shed of a successful inventor. This is where the world's best crimping sleeves are made, as well as his pliers and crimping tools.

The Eze Pull Pliers at work, about to remove a staple. The tool also works as a crimper and wire cutter.

Chris
Taking the strain out of fencing

Shocking as it may seem to anyone for whom Big Mac is an ancestor and not a burger, it has nevertheless been suggested, by a least one eviscerated English wag, that the bagpipes could be the reason so many Scots have emigrated. Alas, the noble Celtic instrument has long been the object of such derision, a target for the barbs of effete types reared on the viol, lute and dulcimer. Not that their jaundiced view cuts much McMustard with those for whom the skirl of the pipes is a sound without peer. Not only is Chris Johnstone one such, but he has more reasons than most to be grateful for Scotland's foremost musical export.

Because, believe it or not, if it hadn't been for the bagpipes he may never have discovered his own inventive talents. But, quite by chance, back in the days when Chris was a farmer he was also a piper. And a very keen one at that. It didn't take him long to find out that farming and piping don't mix. One job in particular, the routine repair and replacement of fences, created all sorts of problems for Chris. 'I found that after stripping fences, I couldn't play the pipes for two weeks,' he says. The reason was simple. Stripping a fence involves pulling all the staples out of all the posts so that old wires can be removed and new wires strung, or to allow the existing fence to be dismantled and another one built. It's hard work, tough on the hands, and the fact that it interfered with his musical passion was a situation Chris couldn't tolerate and wouldn't accept.

When he analysed the problem, one thing very quickly became clear. 'There'd been no development of fencing pliers for a hundred years,' he says. The piper decided that his salvation lay in an implement that could do the job without doing damage to his digits. And eventually, he invented one. 'I finally produced a tool that was so efficient a six-year-old kid could draw out fence staples,' says Chris, 'and really, it's all come from that, the need to draw staples easily.' He called his invention Eze Pull Pliers and quickly found that plenty of other people were as keen to use them as he was.

That was the start of a process that saw him eventually decide to put his money where his mouth was and give up farming to have a go at manufacturing. But even though his original Eze Pull Pliers were a success he knew they could be enhanced and improved. 'That first tool,' he says, 'couldn't join wires. Ultimately, the aim was to have a crimping tool as well.' For the uninitiated, a crimping tool is one that's used to join two lengths of wire so they form a single strand. That can be done with a knot, but it's time consuming and may cause nasty injuries. The alternative is to fit a clasp, or sleeve, over the wires and clamp, or crimp them together. Chris could see that having one tool which would pull out the staples you didn't want, and join up the wires you did, was the ideal solution. 'And it came with the Mark Four,' he says. At last he had a multi-purpose fencing tool. Of course, it's been superseded since. His latest version is the Eze Pull Mark 5, which can crimp any wire up to 2.5 mm.

The piper who's calling the tune, Chris Johnstone has at least one illustrious forebear in the name of Ernest Rutherford. But he doubts there's a strong genetic connection. 'There couldn't be,' he says. 'He was a genius, I'm just a plodder. I'm persistent, that's all. Once I get the smell of something, I stay with it.'

For those with larger strands to link, there's a companion range of specialist crimping tools. A key feature of these is their size. When he began development the current tools were all big, huge things. 'They were awkward, really difficult to use. These ones are small, they're light and with just two crimp notches you can do all types of fence wire.' Well, no, not quite. You'll need to use some of his unique and innovative sleeves as well. Once again, to explain, a 'sleeve' is the piece of metal that slips over two separate pieces of wire, then serves as the 'knot' or 'lock' which holds them together.

So simple a piece of equipment may seem unimportant. But, for anyone who's farming, it isn't. Reliable sleeves are essential if they're to have fences which protect their stock and their livelihood. And the ones that Chris has invented do that better than most. Well no, they do it better than any. Because he's solved a problem that no one else could. And his solution's unique, there's nothing to match it anywhere. 'Most sleeves are made in the United States,' Chris explains, 'and they're all copper.' Trouble is, the copper reacts with the zinc on the galvanising and that causes deterioration. He's overcome that fundamental problem by using a new material, aluminium, to produce his sleeves. 'Others have tried,' he says, 'but they've not had success. These are the first aluminium sleeves to successfully join smooth wire surfaces. They're a world first. The whole thing's a world first, the sleeves and the tool.'

The breakthrough means Chris now figures quite significantly in world production. He's making several thousand tools each year and large volumes of sleeves. About half of what he makes goes overseas, with the US being a major market. His pliers, crimping tools and sleeves also sell well in the United Kingdom and Hungary. He's very proud of his inventions, particularly the crimping sleeves and believes the price and quality have been important elements in their success. Chris manufactures all three products himself, although the body castings for the tools come from a foundry in Auckland.

'I'm very much a commercial character,' he says. 'I start out with an objective, an idea and if I see it's good, I stay with it. A lot of inventors keep on inventing and nothing comes of it. It's one thing to produce a prototype, it's

Some of Chris's range of aluminium crimping sleeves. Chris has managed to find a way that produces sleeves with a common exterior dimension, but varying interior configurations to suit different types of wire. It's a feature others have not been able to emulate.

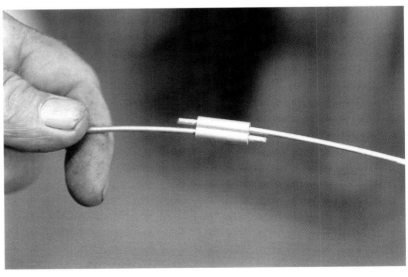

How a crimping sleeve works. The result is a join 15 to 20 percent stronger than a knot.

another to produce a successful commercial product. That's a hell of a lot harder.' Two things are important, Chris believes. One is to make sure there actually is a commercial need for the invention you've produced. The other is to do the development work yourself. And for all that he's determined to keep his feet on the ground, he concedes there's been a strange form of intuition that's driven his investigations. 'I think I've got a bit of a guardian angel helping me. I do the whole thing as an art form. I'm not a numbers person, but I have an ability to know what a piece of steel will do, how it will perform. That design work, that's the art form.'

He doesn't see that talent as unique. Indeed, he regards it as an inherent Kiwi thing. 'I really believe the inventiveness of New Zealanders as engineers means we can hold our head up anywhere in the world.' Part of the reason for that, in his opinion, is that we're so demanding of gear. 'We want gear that holds together, in pretty difficult conditions. That's why the harvester companies send their new products out here to be tested. We use them on hills and banks and rough ground, really thrash them in a way that doesn't happen in America.' Whether his American customers subject his inventions to such rigorous examination is a moot point. If they do, he hasn't had any complaints so far. And no regrets either. He's glad he made the decision to leave farming to his brothers and concentrate on his own creations. He acknowledges the exposure he's had at the Field Days and the fact that they've been a showcase for what he's done. And in the end, he says, 'When I look back, this is the better part of my life's work. This is where I've put my greatest effort and it's where I've had my greatest achievement.'

This close-up shows the varying notches, designed to grip different sized sleeves.

The Eze Pull pliers also crimp narrower gauge wires.

The Eze Crimp tool, with a sleeve in place. It also acts as a cable stripper.

Keith & Tom

Making sure it's invented here

Between them, Keith Stewart and Tom Barter have been inventing for well over a century. And they've probably notched up more than a hundred patents, as well. 'My list stops at sixty-seven,' says Keith. 'I've been inventing since the age of twelve.' He and Tom are both concerned about the quirky image inventors have acquired. Part 'Nutty Professor', part charlatan, it's something they've both battled for years. 'The reputation of inventive people has been tarnished by wild claims and bogus ideas,' says Keith. 'And that,' Tom adds, 'makes it more difficult for able people to get proper attention.'

Tom Barter (left) and Keith Stewart (right). Tom's tree spade is in front of him. Tom is currently editor of the Auckland-based Inventors Trust newsletter, and Keith's an active member also. The Trust's address is Private Bag MBE #248, Auckland.

It's time to put that right. Because both of them are able, and willing, and have readily argued the benefits of New Zealand's inventive culture for years. Whenever they've found a pair of receptive ears. Tom's campaigned for a long time to get changes to the tax laws to allow people to claim genuine R & D expenses. He's not after a loophole into which spurious costs can be slipped, but rather a formula recognising the potential of new ideas and the price of producing them. Especially since it's often lone workers who have to pay it. 'It would bring us in line with the rest of the OECD,' he says. 'We're a stand-alone country in this.' And Keith would like to see New Zealand companies get more involved in the support and development of inventors and inventions.

He's had plenty of experience himself in the fraught business of trying to turn a prototype into a product. So did his dad. 'My father was a very clever engineer,' he recalls. In fact, back in the 1930s he designed what became known as the Edlin Stewart Engine. 'There was much support for it,' says Keith. 'The Bristol aero-engine company were enthusiastic.' But with the death of a prospective financier in an accident, the project withered. The same thing's happened to Keith from time to time, but he's not deterred. Now 82, he's still got drawings of his first successful invention, a valve he produced for an early employer.

Since then, his output's included a powered hand saw, a twin-hull passenger and cargo airship, and a rocker pump that's driven by sails at each end of the beam. 'It's so simple,' he says. 'It cuts out all the mechanical bits of a windmill.' He also designed and built a totally new type of hovercraft. 'Hovercraft have always been damned by three things: noise, stability and controllability. They're hard to control over water and the external propellers make them inherently unstable.' He overcame those problems by driving it with a water jet at the rear.

Keith's self-regulating shower system. The temperature's set by adjusting the nozzle and, once set, won't vary. 'It just hangs in space,' he says. 'There's nothing on the wall at all.'

Airship a winner

Detail from newspaper clipping. Keith's innovative airship design attracted a lot of attention when it was made public.

'And the drive mechanism for the fan was at the front, for balance.' He'd even designed fans on each side which could be operated to allow his machine to tilt into turns.

British hovercraft manufacturers were initially interested in the six to eight-passenger craft, but after a year of talks 'they turned it down'. Keith built the components himself, but not the hull. 'I knew it would clutter up the place for twenty-five years.' All the bits are still in storage but he doubts, at his age, he'll take the project further. 'If someone wanted to take over the technology and develop it, good luck to them.'

He'd like to see something happen with his unique shower head as well. 'That excited a lot of interest when I first invented it. But I haven't found anyone with the money to develop it.' Although he invented it a good long time ago, he doesn't think that, even now, there's anything comparable on the market. His shower has a built-in thermostatic control, that automatically runs it at a pre-set temperature. 'It never varies more than one degree C.' The shower also has an anti-scald provision. 'The hot water can't be turned on till the cold's on.'

Heat's a factor in another of Keith's inventions. But this one harnesses it, rather than protects people from it. Out in the back yard, you'll find the prototype solar pump he's built. Using, amongst other things, a piece of plumbing tube, a camera lens and a detergent bottle lid, this experimental model focuses the sun 'on a little boiler in the centre of the dome'. The boiler produces steam, which passes through a pipe to drive a pump. 'Then the condensate goes back to the boiler, so it's a closed circuit.'

Tom's also produced an ample number of inventions. As a young man, working as a contractor, he came up with his own pile-driving rig, cobbled together with bits and pieces he had at hand. Later, he invented a vibrating concrete screed which cuts the work by 70 percent. 'When I look at my inventions, they're all driven by laziness.' Or a desire to get things done more quickly. Witness his tree spade, the solution to a problem he encountered on his small forestry block. 'In my decrepit state, I could plant 250 a day. And I was too tired to do any the next day. With this, I can do 500 and the next day I'm fresh and ready to work. With this you just stamp it in, push to, push fro, twist to the left, twist to the right and pull it out.'

Both of them are likely to be 'ready to work' to for some considerable time to come. Whatever becomes of whatever they create, they're clearly hooked on inventing. It's a process they enjoy, and you probably couldn't stop them even if you passed a law against it. And, speaking of laws, there appears to be a natural one that doesn't do much to help their cause. 'There's a fatal flaw we're all up against in this country,' says Keith. 'We call it NIH, Not Invented Here. It's a world-wide syndrome, and we've got to work harder than most to overcome it.' You can guarantee they'll keep on trying.

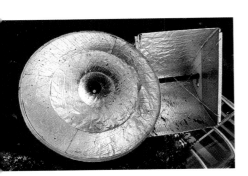

The prototype solar pump, with the dome on the left. Sensors track the sun, correct the azimuth angle, and return the pump to an easterly position at nightfall.

John

A mayor on the move

First prize in the Big Category for 1999 has to go to John Hewitt, farmer, inventor and mayor of the Waipa district. His Worship picks up the award for his Earthmoving Scoop. A whopping great thing it is, as its name suggests, 'for picking up soil and spreading it again'. And doing so well enough to generate healthy demand, although not quite the sort John's after. 'Everyone wants to borrow it. No one wants to buy it.' That's something he plans to change with a manufacturing venture, when he finds time to do it properly. In fact, he'd be spending more time inventing if it weren't for his democratic duties. 'I'd love to dedicate my life to it,' he says, 'if not for the mayoral things. I get great pleasure out of messing round in a shed, building bits and pieces.' That's not to say he doesn't enjoy his work as mayor, because he does. Now in his second term, John says Waipa's a neat area to be involved in. 'It's very compact. There's a hell of a lot in the area for sport and cultural activities and things like that. With 40,000 people we're not too big and we don't have the central government politics and that sort of thing.' The thing is, though, after four years he thought the job might ease off. 'But that's not something that's happened yet.'

The mayor who loves to meddle. A farmer all his life, John's invented post-drivers, a bale grab and a tree pusher called Jaws.

So the inventions will have to wait a while for further development. When they do, his original approach will undoubtedly stand them in good stead. Because John's got a particular and pretty unique area of interest. 'I spent a lot of years involved with earthmoving. That's how I got into the hobby of farm inventions. And I've always had a fascination with hydraulics and how hydraulic power works.' That interest surfaced in an invention he developed and marketed in the early eighties. It was a silage wagon, used for feeding-out on farms, and it did well in New Zealand and Australia. Those on sale at the time used a conveyor belt in the floor to move bales along the wagon to the shredder at the end. The problem was, on hills or uneven surfaces, the bales would roll about, unrestrained. John's solution was a hydraulically driven backing gate to move material down. 'It wasn't tricky on hills, it kept bales secure.'

His interest in hydraulics has persisted and is a feature of his Scoop as well. So is careful planning. 'I spend a huge amount of time considering what I'm going to do before I do it. It's the best way to eliminate risks.' These attributes came into play when John needed to do some earthmoving work and went to buy a piece of equipment. 'But there just wasn't that sort of thing built.' The planning and preparation began. 'The invention,' he says, 'the principle of how it works was the result of hours on a bulldozer with a scoop, working out what geometry makes them work.' When he finally realised what it was he was a trifle surprised. The secret ingredient that gives his Scoop an edge is that simple he can't understand why other people haven't done it.

The point is, they haven't. And that gives John's invention a distinct advantage, namely the ability to hold 'forty to fifty percent more material than you're able to load with a normal scoop'. Since it's built to go behind a large farm tractor that means you can greatly reduce the size of tractor needed. 'You can pull it behind an eighty-five to one hundred horsepower tractor, where you'd normally need a hundred and fifty horsepower large tractor.' Those virtues mean that John is determined to see it go into production at some stage.

In the meantime, there are meetings to chair and fairs to open. But, John says, 'On a really wet day, I must admit fiddling around in the shed is by far my greatest preference. I don't imitate other equipment, I build things that are different. It fires up the enthusiasm to experiment a bit.' And there's nothing that will fire his enthusiasm more than to discover something he hasn't so far. 'I'd love to find something every home needs that only lasts a day. But I haven't got it yet. Still, that's the dream of every inventor, I suppose.'

The Earthmoving Scoop. John built the prototype himself, using materials at hand. He likes stuff built out of scrap. 'I'll use bits and pieces I've got lying round, rather than buy things.'

David

Pumps for the poor

David Barnes and his business development partner have recently made contact with a North Island inventor who's designed a water-powered generator capable of delivering 2.2 kilowatts. Connected to their turbine, it could be used to purify water and still leave more than a kilowatt of power available for other uses.

He's always been 'a sort-of fix-it engineer', someone who 'likes solving problems'. And he may just have solved one of the biggest of them all. Because David's produced an invention that can easily and economically supply water – even power – to the poorest of the poor, wherever they are. All they need is a river and one of his 'very radical' turbines.

The principle's surprisingly simple. 'It surprised me no one had thought of it.' Better yet, David says, 'I could make it out of bamboo, or elephant intestines and reeds if I had to. And it costs nothing to run.'

That's because his turbine relies on water flow. It's actually suspended underwater, supported by floats. On the outside of the central turbine shaft are a series of adjustable arms, which can be extended or contracted. At the outer end of each arm is a hinged blade. These are forced against the arms, with the unit spinning horizontally to produce torque. But, because they're hinged, they'll also swing away from the arm as they revolve, thereby reducing drag. 'The common problem with turbines is drag,' says David. 'This one's the most efficient I've seen.'

David has tested several models and the results are good. 'They do about thirty revolutions a minute. I'm driving my water pump with one and you could certainly drive an electrical system, or a mill, or a washing machine. The turbine's just a drive source really, and you can clip whatever you require to it.' In situations where water flow's insufficient, David envisages a hand-cranked version – 'or solar, or wind, or you could use an animal if you wanted to. Whatever, it's still non-destructive and fish-friendly.'

With obvious remote-area applications, he says the turbine's generated interest from US survival groups 'worried about Y2K problems and the world blowing up, all that carry on'. Yet he's found it much harder to enthuse some more obvious potential users. 'Two billion people could use these as pumps,' insists David. 'They could be made in the country of use, be owned and maintained at village level. But I've found the big aid agencies and governments the least helpful. Billions of dollars go towards water problems, but it's all lip service.'

There's been a better response to some of his other inventions. Canadian authorities are assessing a series of humane traps that he's designed and is putting to good use round his own place to reduce possum numbers. The traps can be tailormade to deal with specific noxious pests. Larger traps are for possums and the like, the smaller ones will eliminate ferrets and weasels. And an American company is evaluating a new safety device as well. It's a gas-filled kite to be used as a locator beacon by anyone lost in the wilderness. 'It takes an aerial up to three hundred feet,' David explains. The kite 'could use some radar reflective material, or possibly have spray-on solar panels to work at night. That one's progressing quite quickly in the US.'

He's even 'got some people who might be interested' in his latest thing, a high-speed wheel with no axle. There are drawings but, at this stage, they're definitely not for publication. Suffice to say, he thinks he's progressed beyond the caveman's Mark 1 wheel by devising a stub attachment that can go anywhere you like. 'It moves the whole centre of gravity. It would be impossible to flip a car with these fitted.'

Whether this tantalising prospect ever makes it commercially remains uncertain. David's quick to admit he's not a businessman. 'I'm a designer. I've had some ideas that are truly mind-boggling, but I've never developed them.' Like the collapsible kayak he produced twenty years ago. 'It could go on your back as a pack. It took five minutes to put it together, no nuts, bolts or screws, and ninety seconds to pull it apart. You could also clip them together and use them as a catamaran. They're still the lightest kayaks in the world . . . I made about two dozen of them. I should've probably done more with that. Maybe, one day, I'll get back to it . . .'

But for now there's the turbine. And the traps. And the kite. And the Mark 2 Superwheel. Not to mention the Advanced Technologies Group he's just joined. That takes up time as well, although it's put him in touch with some exciting notions. 'You see some pretty clever things in New Zealand,' says David, 'and some very clever people out there.' The impartial observer would say he's one of them, but his own analysis is a little more rigorous. 'I'm heading in a direction . . . but I wouldn't say it's the right direction.' Well, maybe not, but I've got my fingers crossed.

David's traps feature a bait box with two panels vertically mounted at the front. The bottom panel is fixed, the top is spring-loaded. A possum, for example, will put its head through the central aperture to reach the bait. Then, when it pulls out, the head movement trips the spring. The top panel clamps down, cutting off both air and blood supply, killing the animal in about 90 seconds.

Carston Fitjer

David's turbine being raised from the river after a test run. The hinged blades are the key to its efficiency.

Don

If it is broke, don't sell it

Julian Brown

Mr Chairman. Some 27 years of involvement with Mystery Creek – and twelve years in charge of the Inventors Awards – give Don Heaslip a better appreciation than most of the abundant ingenuity abroad in the land.

Mystery Creek's quite possibly the biggest thing for agriculture since refrigerated shipping. And definitely the biggest thing for the Waikato since the Mooloo Song – *Olé Olé Olé*. The Field Days are now such a massive exercise that any intrepid explorer who wants to see the whole show would need to take extra rations, sturdy boots, thick socks and a sleeping bag. With the event now featuring no less than 1000 exhibitors' stands, those with a fondness for time and motion studies have calculated that even if someone only spent 60 seconds at each display, it would still take two and a half days to do the full tour of inspection.

One of the big attractions at Mystery Creek is the wide range of prototypes, inventions and new releases on show. Don Heaslip's been Chairman of the Inventors Awards at the Field Days for twelve years and every year, he says, something stands out as the big hit. This year, he's picking it will be a new organic weedkiller made from pure pine tree oil. 'It's a New Zealand idea,' Don says, 'and it's going to be big. It'll kill moss and wasps as well as weeds because it's got such a high pH level.'

He's well placed to assess the merits of new ideas and inventions. He's come up with quite a few of his own over the years, some of which have gone on to be that most elusive of things, a commercial success. He's got high hopes one of the current crop will be as well. It's a kind of shower for sheep and it's Don's answer to the massive problem of flystrike. The disagreeable tendency of flies to lay their eggs in sheep's wool can be crippling financially, and for the animals. 'The maggots eat into them, they get blood poisoning and other things. The sheep can suffer terribly.' So can a farmer's bank account. 'They estimate that $140,000,000 is lost annually through flystrike,' says Don.

The Sheep Cradle takes the choresomeness out of crutching. Instead of heaving and hauling, a finger tip tilts the rig to give easy access to a woolly derriere. The Cradle's been picked up by a manufacturer and is now commercially available.

There are products on the market to fight flystrike. But they can cost several thousand dollars. Don estimates his would sell at 'around a thousand, possibly a bit less'. A bit of animal psychology's been applied to the design which really relies on the behaviour of sheep. 'Once you get them started, they'll all follow the leader. If the first sheep goes through a particular hole in the fence, all the others will go in through the same hole.' Exploiting that tendency, his ovine ablutions are designed like 'a pitchfork with no middle prong' so there's no visible barrier. Installed in a sheep race, the unit has a lever triggered as each sheep moves forward. That opens the ball valve to give each sheep a measured squirt of essential chemicals.

The flystrike shower in use in a race. Note the two pitchfork-style prongs, with a gap in the centre which encourages the sheep to head where they're supposed to. The animal's movement trips a lever that activates the spray. The invention's a low-cost solution to a perennial problem in New Zealand agriculture.

Crutching rather than chemistry is at the heart of a second invention. Don remembers how tough it was to tackle a large flock. The cradle's been invented to eliminate the hard work of 'going into the pen, pulling one out, crutching and just doing that all day'. With the cradle installed in a race, the sheep go up and into it. 'You can pull it over with one finger because the balance point's right, then crutch and dag the sheep. You can do the feet if you want to. And pregnancy tests as well. It's good for animal health things.'

Anything he designs has to pass one or two simple tests. 'It's got to be idiot proof to be a proper invention,' he says. And it's got to be reliable. 'I do not make products that are shoddy.' Before he attempts to put any invention on the market, it gets a very thorough workout on his own farm. 'We give them heaps. We try to wreck them. If we can't, we know we've got a pretty good product.' He's saddened by the lack of funding in New Zealand. 'People come up with these brilliant ideas but when it comes to develop them, they haven't got $50,000 so they just throw it under the table. It's a shame really.' Then again, he's proved it can be done, despite the hurdles. The success of an invention is something he savours. 'Seeing a product go on the market is great, it's good to see that. That's the thing I enjoy most, seeing things made and out there and doing well.'

Another invention Don was involved with that's now on the market is this weed wiper. The unit rises and falls as it comes into contact with plants. Before use, it's set to operate at a predetermined height. This ensures the pump-driven wick delivers its chemical dose at that height, but no other. As long as the operator knows the height of the weeds to be eliminated, they can be got rid of without harming other plants.

Sandy

There's got to be a better way

'The status quo is no more than a good place to begin.' That's been Sandy's philosophy for years. It's why he invents things and why, at the age of 76, he can't see himself stopping. By his own admission, it's a compulsion. 'When I look at anything, I think "Is that the best way that can be done?" It seems to be a part of me. I can't help it.' He thinks two things in particular have fuelled this irresistible drive. One is being brought up in the back blocks of the bush. 'If you wanted something you had to make it yourself, or you didn't get it.' The other is his involvement with the Mystery Creek Field Days for nearly 30 years.

Sandy Chesswas with two of his hand-held weed wipers. Chemicals are stored in a dispenser screwed into the top of the wand, then dispensed in the same way as nips are served in hotels. The system ensures optimum chemical use and Sandy doesn't think it's too complicated. 'We just did the whole farm for nodding thistle,' he says. 'It was five minutes' effort to get rid of weeds.'

Seeing other people's ideas and inventions has encouraged him to keep on creating his own.

Indeed, one of his first inventions got an award at the Field Days. He'd seen a vet being kicked by a cow while doing a pregnancy test. So he produced a restrainer to prevent injury. That's typical of his approach. Sandy's an inventor who'll tackle anything. 'It doesn't matter what it is, if something's needed, I just make it.' He recalls, a few years ago, his church planned to spend a considerable sum on electric motors to open and close their high windows. 'I said, "Don't be silly." I devised a cheap way to open them from the bottom.' He used an eccentric and a spring and some fishing line. 'When you pull the line, the eccentric goes across centre and the spring pushes the window open or pulls it shut. It's still working now.'

And so is his vertical clothes-line. Invented two years ago, he thought 'it could have a future in places like Singapore and Hong Kong, where everyone lives in high-rise buildings'. Aware that space is something apartment dwellers don't have a lot of, Sandy designed the line 'to invert, so you could retire it against a wall'. A quick turn of 'a little handle' takes the clothes-line from vertical to horizontal and back, and it can also be raised and lowered.

'It's very simple,' he says, 'but I don't think it's been done before.' Full of enthusiasm, he attempted to contact a manufacturer but there was no reaction. 'I never heard from them so I haven't bothered with it any more. Public relations and marketing are not one of my attributes.'

'That means a lot of his inventions stay as prototypes, useful for him but not necessarily saleable in that form. Like his microwave stirrer, which he thinks 'is an idea waiting for someone to pick up'. Although, for the moment, he's quite content to use it himself. And does so, every day. As he says, 'If I can't cook it in the microwave, I don't eat it.' But when he found his porridge was coming out lumpy, a solution was clearly required. The one he's come up with is just using the torque in the microwave itself. 'As the microwave goes round, the liquid gets stirred. A manufacturer might need to check to see there's enough torque, but it's never let me down.'

'A bit like a coathanger,' Sandy's microwave stirrer straddles the turntable. The central shaft supports a horizontal blade, which keeps unwelcome lumps out of porridge and the like.

The fruit and vegetable peeler has obvious benefits for arthritis sufferers. It is fixed in the sink with suction cups, food items are held on the shaft and the whole unit revolves with peelings all going into the sink.

Nor has his fruit and vegetable peeler. Held in place with suction cups, the peeler 'plonks into the sink' and ensures that 'all the residue stays there' as well. While these are all inventions Sandy's designed and built himself, he also collaborates with others. Along with another Mystery Creek veteran, Don Heaslip, he's produced a commercially successful sheep handling cradle and a popular, large weed wiper that's towed behind a tractor. But not content with one, Sandy's also invented a second, smaller, hand-held wiper. This one's a tilt up, tip down design that works the same way it does when you go to the pub for a whisky. 'They tip the bottle up so that a measured amount of whisky comes down. This is exactly the same principle. To get the chemicals down from the top, you've got to go up first.'

Sometimes, Sandy says, 'Things come to me in the middle of the night.' He woke up one morning at about 2 a.m. with the image of a Japanese fan in his mind. He suddenly realised it was the ideal form for a sheep gate 'with no latch and no hinges that would still stop a sheep in seconds flat' and incorporated the idea in a sheep shearing cradle he's still testing at present. 'It's great to see something work that you've made up as a concoction,' he says. 'It's just my kinky sort of brain, I suppose. I'm determined to do better than what's there now.'

Stowing the vertical clothes-line requires minimal room. Sandy calls it 'a spiderweb' because the individual lines are 'close enough to be used as a double so you need fewer pegs'. He says there's enough space for two double sheets and the rest of the washing.

Still under development, Sandy's sheep handler has potential for shearing. There's 'all sorts of fine-tuning to do' but 'it could have a future'.

Jim Hopkins Author

It has often been said that if Jim Hopkins didn't exist, it would be necessary not to invent him. Be that as it may, the fact is he does exist and for years the authorities have struggled to find some useful purpose to which he can be applied. *Blokes and Sheds* and *Inventions from the Shed* are increasingly seen by many in psychotherapeutic circles as the answer. His new-found role as chronicler of the unchronicled at least gets him out of the house, to the enormous relief of those who remain in it. Although his own inventive talents have been largely applied to concocting semi-plausible reasons to get off speeding tickets, he has had an abiding interest in the area. More years ago now than he cares to remember, he hosted two series of 'The UDC Inventors Awards' on New Zealand television and still believes it's an area that doesn't attract the attention it should. If this book helps to change that situation he believes it will have achieved something quite important. With two books now completed, he has plans for a third although, given the demands of the literary life, he may opt for a nervous breakdown instead. A well-known and popular public speaker and debater, Jim currently makes a weekly appearance on TVNZ's 'Breakfast' programme and also contributes the occasional documentary when the effects of the medication have worn off.

Julie Riley Photographer

Anna Riley

Now widely regarded as the Cartier-Bresson of shed society, Julie Riley's gone behind the lens again to put the best of the back yard in the picture. Her own inventive temperament is clearly evident in her black and white studies of gadgets and gizmos, not to mention gidgets and gazmos. And her work's also attracting critical attention. Writing in the *Arts Grants Weekly* one generously funded reviewer said, 'These translucent eviscerations of essence and portent generate a metaphorical fusion, an elemental dialogue whose elliptic pastiche revisits the central peripheries of visualised semiotics.' The arts column of *Plumbing News* puts it more clearly. 'No one understands a widget better than Julie.' And the photographs prove the point. *Inventions from the Shed* is Julie's second collaboration with Jim Hopkins and while she remains deeply suspicious of his driving, there are plans for a third. She has also written and photographed two books of her own, *Men Alone* and *Our Town*. Like the book in your hands now, they were studies of unseen and perhaps undervalued aspects of New Zealand society. When she is not producing books or escaping to her favourite bach, Julie heads the Professional Photography School within the Art and Design Department of Christchurch Polytechnic.